TELLING TALES

Celebrating

Coventry, UK City of Culture 2021

By the
COVENTRY WRITERS' GROUP

Introduction by the *Lord Mayor of Coventry, Cllr John McNicholas.*
"Coventry is a city full of great stories – and great storytellers, and this book is a real treasure. I couldn't put "Telling Tales" down until I'd read from cover to cover.

Different writers and different styles all blend together to create a joyous tribute to Coventry, UK City of Culture 2021. If you love Coventry, this book is a must, and if you don't yet know our city, then you'll want to come and visit us after reading this book.

"Telling Tales" reflects the true multi-cultural, welcoming nature of our City. Heart-warming, poignant and a reminder of why I decided to live in Coventry with the Lady Mayoress forty plus years ago. To cap it all if you look on the front cover you can see my former office overlooking the Cathedral ruins!

A lovely book, well written and a must for all in our year as Coventry City of Culture 2021.

*

Foreword by Maxine Burns, Chair of Coventry Writers' Group.
For more than 60 years the Coventry Writers' Group has helped to hone the talents of poets, playwrights, novelists and short story writers. The group has been there to provide inspiration through mixing with other creatives with the aim of getting their work placed in a variety of outlets, and many have elevated a hobby into a lucrative career.

As a group, we have published a number of anthologies, one of which won an award for Best Writers' Circle Anthology by Writing Magazine. We are proud to present our latest medley of stories, poems and articles written by some members of the group to mark the city becoming UK City of Culture 2021.

The CWG has always welcomed all calibre of writers be they complete novices, multi-published, or anywhere in between. It offers enthusiasm, support and advice to all.

We hope you enjoy reading this book as much as we have enjoyed writing it.

Content

SO GLAD I WAS 'SENT TO COVENTRY'

By Alex Bartlett

You're being sent to Coventry.

I've heard it so many times from people who thought they were being funny that I decided to look it up:

The term, meaning *to be ignored or ostracised,* most likely originating around the 17th century when prisoner troops during the English Civil war were sent to Coventry and not accepted, has turned into a joke. But for me, a boy from a small town in leafy Surrey, Coventry is where I found myself, became a man and made my home, career and family.

Before I came here, I was aware of Coventry, but mainly through the football team who were a regular fixture in the Premiership back then, but never thought I'd end up living here.

But when, as a teenager doing what many teenagers do (I'm talking about looking at higher education here!) it became one of my top choice universities, offering a brilliant media course. I also liked the fact that while it was a much bigger, more interesting place to live than the tiny town I'd grown up in, it lacked the overcrowded, intimidating feel of some of the bigger cities I'd visited. Coventry felt like a friendly, welcoming place to be. And none of the other universities inspired me as much as Coventry did. When I got my acceptance letter after the traditionally nervous wait – I was over the moon.

I enjoyed University so much, made many good friends and met a girl who would change me for the better, forever. I was born abroad and spent a lot of my time feeling a bit lost and confused by the mix of culture around me, but Coventry was different. I no longer felt awkward and geeky – I felt like I'd found a place to be me.

Yes, there were times when I was homesick and tempted to run back to the family bubble – as felt by everyone as they leave the parental nest for the first time (and not just to raid the larder and get my ironing done!) but it was the happiest I'd ever been. When I graduated with a 2:1, I was pleased with it and felt I had the world at my feet.

That girl I mentioned above, well she finished top of her class with a great degree too – and was just crazy enough to say yes when I produced a ring and a certain question, which was an incredible feeling. She had been job hunting all over the country – neither of us really wanting to become part of the London rat race after our time in the Midlands. When an opportunity came up in Coventry, it seemed perfect. Plus, I still had university friends living here, and I couldn't wait to get back.

We lived in a shared flat in Holbrooks first. After about a month of job hunting, I got a sales job with a small newspaper company called JCP (Journal Publishing Company) in the City Centre. This would be the start of my Coventry career. Soon I moved onto working at the Coventry Telegraph in sales, and thoroughly enjoyed it there (which had nothing to do with the free beers and meals offered to me as lead contributor to the Diners Directory – honest). I made more good friends and enjoyed seeing the adverts and features I'd created.

We bought our first home in Bell Green aged twenty-two: just a small '70s maisonette needing tonnes of work, but we were on the property ladder. We had settled here, my friends and career were here, and going back to my parents' house would only be for special occasions and passing visits. I felt settled and had created a home.

I married the love of my life in St Mary's Guildhall followed by photos in the old cathedral close by, and then outside the University building that had brought us all together. My best man I met in my part-time student job, while my ushers were my close university friend and brother-in-law to be.

Our wedding was an incredible occasion. The looks on our guests' faces when they walked into the main hall of the

Guildhall were of amazement with the beauty of the place. I thought getting married in a place that had been the Houses of Parliament in the 13th Century was cool and unique (I believe Coventry is the only place outside of London to have the Houses of Parliament) – so much so that I booked the venue before my wife had viewed it. I got away with it, because we both knew it and I knew she loved it. And for us, there was no other option then a Coventry wedding.

I just love the history of this city, from Lady Godiva to the blitz spirit and rebuilding of the cathedral following bombings; from Queen Elizabeth 1 visiting to Coventry having a castle, and how its people have overcome so much adversity. St John's Baptist Church on Corporation Street (which was where the King's soldiers were imprisoned and ignored in the 17th century and the phrase *Sent to Coventry* likely came from), still stands tall in the city centre. Coventry is a worthy recipient of the capital of culture award.

I've enjoyed attending various events in Coventry such as the annual Godiva Festival. Coventry City matches at the Ricoh Arena and Highfield Road – which was just a minute's walk from my uni house back in 2003/4. I attended regularly and they've certainly become my 2nd team – sorry, you can blame my parents for the Reds! I always preferred Highfield over the Ricoh, as it was such a tight-knit ground and the atmosphere was brilliant, whereas the Ricoh, though much improved facilities, often felt soulless. Though I've been to some brilliant events there such as Bruce Springsteen – even getting to play football there.

I left the Coventry Telegraph to work at the travel company TUI UK and again, made more friends and had some interesting experiences, including going to Egypt for an *Educational* to learn about the hotels we were promoting to our customers (just in time to get a tan before my wedding). After a few more years, I moved to working at the exam board OCR. Just as I left there for a promotion with another company, I got run over. Yes, you've read that right, I got run over whilst out running on one of the main arterial roads for the city shutting down half the city and making it onto local radio.

Walsgrave hospital got me back walking and running again in a relatively short time after plenty of physiotherapy, and I'm grateful for everything they've done.

I joined a local running club in 2013 and my friends there helped me get running again after the accident, which has been a passion of mine for a long time. Plus, it gave me another reason to be up here, instead of just home and work, and I'm still enjoying being a member of the club (my wife prefers me running with friends too, following the accident, so win-win).

After nearly a decade we left our Bell Green home and moved to a nearby village in Warwickshire. (Yes, I know it's technically not Coventry, but it's still very close and is a great village). The people are friendly and the house is lovely, so much bigger than our maisonette. We feel this will be our family home and here we can get the benefits of country life, whilst knowing Coventry city centre is only 20-minutes' drive away. Plus, my work is 10-minutes' drive from my new job at a well-known delivery provider.

Coventry has changed while we've been here, but I still love it and can't see me living anywhere else. Thanks for embracing this southerner, Coventry, and making me feel more at home here than anywhere else in the world. I feel like an honorary Midlander now.

So, you can see why being *Sent to Coventry* was the best thing that ever happened to me, and why I'm proud to call it my home.

BIG MIKE'S GIFT

By Taffi Nyawanza

Arriving in Coventry from Zimbabwe

It is late summer in southwest Coventry and evening is falling. The bees are dive-bombing the detritus of our cook-out; discarded cans and bottles, paper plates, bones, uneaten sadza and salads. Below us, the women are chatting and laughing amidst the task of gathering and cramming these into black plastic bags which they tie and pile up around the overflowing bins.

I am standing on the patio with Big Mike, my neighbour. I ladle a fat sausage straight from the barbecue stand to his paper plate. He bends forward, squeezes his eyes and twists his neck to take a bite.

"I'm absolutely digging this, bro. And dude, stop not inviting me to your barbecues next time," he says through a mouthful, even though he has never required an invitation to my stoep whenever I throw a cook-out or BBQ as he calls it – which is every weekend when it does not rain.

"You, sir, are the bees' knees, you know that?" he says and licks his thick fingers of jerk sauce, one after the other.

In the garden, the kids are squealing and running and squirting their bright water guns at each other and at the golden retriever which shakes out its coat and nips at their heels.

My daughter runs up to where we are standing. "Daddy, can I have a dog? Pleeease!" she says, her hands held out together in front of her and her eyes turned up to heaven in exaggerated supplication. "Oh, I just love me a dog," she adds and scampers off after the retriever.

"She will be bothering me about that the whole week now," I say accusingly to Big Mike who is dog-sitting the retriever for his elderly mother during her occasional retreat to Lourdes. "Always happens when you bring that darn dog here."

"Forget dogs, bro," Big Mike says. "You don't want the hassle. You can't handle it. Dogs are companions for lonely white people." He shouts to be heard above the thump of Chimurenga music coming from the beat box perched on the window ledge.

Big Mike is one of those white people who fist-bumps black people and says "yo, bro," as a badge of his PC credentials.

*

The first day Big Mike introduced himself at my door when we moved into the neighbourhood, he thrust a Coor into my face like an offering and said, "You know, I'm practically coloured. I have a coloured great-grandparent on my mother's side of the family."

The startled wariness of that day has now evolved to an ambivalent tolerance, eased somewhat by a shared love-hate relationship with Arsenal. And our shared cook-outs. And it mellowed me towards Coventry. My first day in the city had decidedly hardened me towards it.

We had arrived by late bus and went to look for food in the city centre. Afterwards, we walked up the hill, back to the little hotel with the self-cleaning shower rooms where we had put up, laden with plenty of unbelievably cheap fried wings and other meats that the chap serving had shaved off a rotating stump.

We were enjoying our leisurely stroll, taking in our new surroundings in the fading, but still warm, light. We saw the cathedral ruins that first evening, its spectral spire bathed in a magical, ambient light that seemed to come from below ground. We were suitably, immediately impressed.

Suddenly, near the roundabout which marks the city limits and where the road to the hotel begins, a small car screamed past us. The youthful occupants of the vehicle hung out from the rolled down windows and lifted their fingers in crude gestures that we had only seen on American TV shows, while they screamed, "Go back home, Kunta."

*

It was Big Mike, strangely enough, with his self-invitations and brash race analysis who changed me.

"I can tell you this, from a vantage point, white people have no concept of family beyond the immediate unit of spouse and the kids. You guys get it; you just don't know how blessed you are to have this." He waved around, as if to indicate the evidence of what he was talking about. He was tackling a juicy spare rib; it dangled from his hand in that careless manner of the sated. In the other hand was an almost empty Coor.

Big Mike refers to white people as *them* as though he is a disinterested bystander who has attained racial nirvana.

"We have our issues," I said to him.

"Who doesn't? We have far worse. Pakistanis have forced marriages. Indians have the caste. The Chinese have triads and snakeheads. Nigerians have yahoo boys. Jamaicans have..."

"I get it, yes," I laughed.

"Ganja," he shouted.

"What?"

"Ganja. Jamaicans like ganja."

Big Mike was wrong of course. Not about ganja – about dogs. I had, in fact, thought very briefly about getting a dog, but shelved the idea immediately when I considered my crazy work shift-patterns, then the crazy budget for dog food and the vet fees and then the crazy daily walk routines, one in the morning and another in the evening, or even three like Pam at number 19. And where would the dog sleep anyway? But the biggest thing was trying to forget that thing at the airport.

I had gone to Africa and arrived back at Birmingham airport looking the part in a colourful Kwame Nkrumah shirt and Jesus sandals. My hair was suitably awry to suit. I was going for the *revolutionary protest poet* look. I was promptly asked to stand aside by a policeman with a sniffer dog. My bags were duly sniffed.

"Open them, sir," said the officer with that tone of voice which is polite and stern at the same time.

"Did you pack your own bags, sir?" added his colleague who had joined us and holding on to a dog whose tail was wagging very fast.

"Yes, my mother helped me," I said, pulling out my prized peanut butter, biltong, billets of sugar cane and dried chomolia. Besides us, as I continued to empty my bags, my fellow travellers waltzed past in their smart dress shirts and polished shoes.

"I'm afraid we have to impound these, sir. They are on the banned substances list," an immigration officer who had also joined the party said, her thin and straight nose in the air. She lifted my oily peanut butter with two gloved fingers and sealed it in a clear plastic bag and threw it in a big black bin. She did the same with the sugarcane and the chomolia.

I blamed the dog enough to not want one in my house. Ever!

*

At the next cook-out, Big Mike sets down a small box, perforated on the sides. He opens it and reaches down very deliberately, like a magician.

"This is for you, Gugu," he says. My daughter screams and receives her gift. She lifts it up like Mufasa lifting up Simba to the ancestors. The puppy gives a feeble yelp and I look into its big eyes. Big mistake. The last vestiges of canine resistance that I have harboured simply melt.

SQUARE WHEELS AND DIAMANTÉ THONGS

By Emilie Lauren Jones

A teenager growing up in Coventry

We were the Naughties kids.
We were happy anywhere that had a sofa –
her Nan's front room, his garden,
the Canal Basin bin shed...
Passing kids were potential friends,
we invited them in to share our batches.

We were the Naughties kids.
We made dens out of our best bed sheets
and upside-down clothes horses.
We raced out of school gates to meet
by the brook with the fraying rope swing
and used the 'no ball games' signs as goalposts.

We were the Naughties kids.
Our school shirts flapped open, revealing
glow stick coloured crop tops, while hip-kissing
diamanté thongs dared teachers to comment.
We drank the left-over wine in cookery class
and threw pig hearts at Ofstead inspectors.

We were the Naughties kids.
We tagged ring-road bridges with
scooter skid marks until friction turned
the wheels square.
We sprayed our stories onto subway walls,
signed our names in cement.

We were the Naughties kids.
We modelled Primark's latest range
as we snuck into JJ's or arranged secret meetings
over MSN when our parents weren't using the phone.
We showed off our tongues in every photo
and they remain as childhood memorials
on our long logged out of MySpace pages...

We are the Naughties kids.
We work in garages, hospitals, shops...
we teach children how to count,
and add tins to the foodbank.
And sometimes,
we drink too much, stay out too late,
and sleep anywhere that has a sofa.

MOONLIGHT SONATA

By David Court

The path of a simple piece of launched metal, be it bullet or shell, can change the trajectory of the world. A single round fired in the right place, at the right time, at the right person, can result in the launching of a trillion more.

As the cartridges (3.7 inches thick, 14.7 inches long) rolled down the noisy Coventry production line, did any of the workers ever pause to contemplate their sole grim purpose? They looked unremarkable – battleship grey with bronze banding and dull silver nose cones. One, however, had a notable destiny.

Did any of the young packers, piling cartridge-filled crates into awaiting lorries, think of the contents? Suspect that just one of those cartridges could make a difference? Not all trajectories are world-shattering, but all are significant to somebody. And one – just one, mind – 3.7" Anti-aircraft shell would make a considerable difference to one very particular set of men.

*

There was a reverence to it, ceremony of sorts. There were strict rituals to be adhered to, and they all knew it. Even the most God-fearing of them would claim to hold little truck with superstition, but, unlike many of their Luftwaffe companions, they were still alive – and who were they to say that these silly rites and practices weren't partly responsible for that?

Oswald was always the first to enter, clambering into the cramped cockpit. Only when he was seated and the photo of his sweetheart stuck with gum to the Plexiglass of the cockpit window, were the others permitted to sit down. Wilhelm was next, sliding into the front gunner's seat next to Oswald.

Gunter and Karl, Radio Operator and Observer respectively, were next. It was only when they were all seated, belts wrapped tightly across beige jumpsuits, that they were permitted to speak.

"I swear it used to be a different woman each time," laughed Wilhelm, pointing at the grainy black and white photograph of the buxom blonde bombshell adorning the pilot's cockpit. Oswald smiled and said nothing, preferring to concentrate on his instruments. The whole plane vibrated and trembled as it came to life, twin propellers spinning into action, a days' worth of dust shaken loose in moments. The Great Bird was waking up.

"Oswald!" shouted Gunter, straining to be heard over the now roaring engines of the Dornier, "I thought you were Luftwaffe born and bred? You're supposed to drop your payload and move on!"

Karl, rustling through the pile of papers and maps in the folder that sat on his knees, shook his head in dismay.

"Leave such talk for the Officer's Mess, gentlemen," he said, in that deep voice that could silence a room. He was the oldest of them all by a good ten years, and there were occasions when he had to remind them of their duties. The plane fell silent, save for Gunter – who always had to have the last word – imitating the whistling sound of a descending bomb.

Karl tutted, turning his attention to the map.

*

The cockpit, usually only illuminated by the dull lighting of instruments, was bathed in the iridescent glow of a brilliant full moon. At times it would flicker, another plane in loose formation passing between them and it, but for the most part it shone down as a blazing sentinel. The Atlantic beneath them lay still and calm, a far cry from the tumult passing eight thousand feet overhead.

Half a thousand Luftwaffe German Bombers from Luftloffe 3 and the pathfinders from Kampfgruppe 100 ploughed a course towards the English coast, one of the most audacious air exercises of the war to date. Everywhere Oswald looked, the sky was filled with their distinctive silhouettes, moonlight glinting against glass and metal. If their own engines weren't so loud that they had to shout to be heard, they would have noticed the air was filled with a long, drawn-out single note, the harmonics of a thousand propellers. This distinctive tone, this perpetual hum of the airborne war machine, was the symphony of what they all knew to be the Mondscheinsonate – the Moonlight Sonata.

There was darkness beneath them now, but that would be short-lived. It would soon change to the desperate shifting beams of searchlights, to the inevitable infernal maelstrom of SC50 bombs turning concrete and steel to ash.

It was early evening on the 14th of November 1940. Every pilot, every gunner, every radio operator had a single goal, a sole target – the industrial city of Coventry.

*

It was the lull before the storm – or more precisely, the lightning war – the Blitzkrieg.

Wilhelm Wellenbrock, Gunner, prayed. Even though his God was omniscient and knew his every thought, it felt peculiar not to say the words of the prayer out loud as he remembered them. He was careful not to mutter them loudly for fear that Karl would hear, and the two of them would be drawn into another long and laborious shouted theological discussion. Wilhelm was in no mood for an argument this evening. He closed his eyes and clutched at the crucifix in his pocket, praying for their safe return.

Gunter Kuhne, Radio Operator, was not ready. He had been full of youthful bravado for most of the day, but now he came to think of it, trapped in this metal shell heading for the heart of his enemy, he was scared. As he checked the radio frequencies on his equipment for the fifth time in as many minutes, he could see his hands shaking even through the thick gloves. He stared at his feet, trying desperately not to be sick.

Karl Dilthey, Observer, could see Wellenbrock's mouth moving in silent prayer. Truth be told, only this time last year he'd have been doing the same. War, however, had torn the faith from him. There were Engländers now, beneath their flight path, praying to the same God that their cannon fire would strike true.

And here was Wellenbrock, praying for the opposite. It made no sense, so it was easier – and more logical – to believe in nothing. Just war and the evil that men do to each other - It may have been cynical, but it kept him sane.

Oswald Preiss, Pilot, stared into the monochrome face of his lover. It was a photo from a time before the war, the day he'd proposed. It was worn and creased now, passed from barracks to cockpit and back again. They were happy then, the two of them. Even with the poor quality of the crumpled photograph and its distorted contours, he could see the glint in her eyes – the life that burned within her. As Oswald had returned to the skies and their engagement grew ever longer, he could see the glint fading. She was with her family in Dresden now, hopefully a million miles away from the wars to come.

*

There would be other stories, this night. Some would sing of heroism, and some would whisper of abject cowardice. Some stories would end before they had barely begun, young lives snuffed out in their prologue. Some tales thought ended were revived, extraordinary acts by ordinary people.

And some stories, as many do, would remain unknown. How Tommy "Tommo" Watson, baby-faced Butcher's apprentice only conscripted three days prior – with his first ever go on an anti-aircraft gun – was the only person who downed an aircraft that night. And never knew it, thinking his shot had missed.

Tommo lived a long yet unspectacular life, blissfully unaware of the spectacular thing that he'd achieved. An anecdote that could have been milked for free ales at the Golden Cross for a lifetime remained unmilked, existing only as a lie told by those who knew it to be a lie.

*

The dotted, spaced-out lights of the English coast became the spattered stardust nebulae of towns, which in turn erupted into the crowded constellations of cities. And with the cities came the inevitable searchlights, oak-trunk thick beams of light to guide the waiting anti-aircraft gunners. Like the outstretched tentacles of some mighty luminous leviathan, they grabbed at the heavens.

Below them, illuminated by the magnesium-bright shafts of light, were the bloated forms of barrage balloons. The height of each bomber's approach was well planned to keep them safe from these deadly inflatables, but any pilot worth his salt was scanning the horizon, looking for any rogue strays that might have drifted into their flightpath.

Woe betide the bomber that fell foul of the thick metal cable below each balloon, the weight of it easily capable of bringing a plane down. But barrage balloons were slow, easily spotted – and, therefore, easily avoided.

But they served their purpose, which was to keep the bombers as high as possible – which made them easier targets for the concentrated anti-aircraft fire from below.

The only sound noisier than the whining of their engines was the cacophony of the firestorm that erupted around them. Anti-aircraft shells lit up the skies, pulsing strobes of magnesium, a lethal blossom of explosive bursts scattered like flowers across their flight path. Gunter winced with each vibration of the Dornier's hull; the sound of each of his involuntary whimpers thankfully masked by the accompanying explosive noise.

More light sources joined the kaleidoscope of brilliance that greeted the Luftwaffe's unwelcome arrival – the pathfinder bombers chosen to lead the pack had performed their tasks with precision and valour, dropping their flares and incendiaries to light up the various target areas dotted around the mostly unprepared city.

The cloudless night sky above Coventry was almost as bright as day, a thousand thunder-flashes bursting overhead. The orchestra of air-raid sirens barely drowned out the sound of the bombers, a long monotone drone that would haunt the dreams of survivors for years to come. The sky was filled with bombers, horizon to horizon, as though the Germans had sent every plane in their arsenal to this Midlands city.

Thomas "Tommo" Watson's eyes were frozen on the awe-inspiring sight above him, and it took one of his comrades to tap him on the shoulder to angrily remind him of where he was, who he was. Collecting himself as best he could and taking a deep breath, he clambered into the gunner's seat of the QF 3.7-inch AA gun.

The three dozen anti-aircraft guns dotted around Coventry thumped like jackhammers, each pulsed thud signifying a new shell launched into the heavens. Tommo's gun joined the evensong chorus, his chair vibrating with each shot, threatening to shake the teeth from his jaw.

The first verse of the Moonlight Sonata was reaching its end; the background of bomber engines and propellers accompanied by the percussive blasts of skyborne shells. But then came the chorus, the predictable entry of the wind section.

The dreaded whistling of descending bombs, the plummeting of destructive ordnance.

*

It would not be the first time that Coventry was bombed during World War II, nor would it be the last. But it would be the most significant, an event etched into history, carved deep with craters and fire.

During the First World War, it was revealed that much of Coventry's mechanical tooling industry could be adapted to war production purposes. The same was true for the Second World War, with Coventry ending up being a major production centre for aircraft, ordnance, and munitions.

These factories were the Germans' target; an attempt to land a major blow against the allies' ability to contribute to the war effort. However, as with many industrial towns in the West Midlands, the streets that held the factories were interlaced into the same streets as worker's houses, and logically, the shops they shopped in, the pubs they drank in.

For that evening and much of the next morning, on the streets of Coventry, the earth itself opened, and Hell spewed out. Bombs erupted across the city; a staccato drum rhythm pounded from five hundred drums to join the Sonata.

*

Oswald Preiss and his crew were in the first wave of bombers. These were armed with explosive ordnance − 16 SC50 fragmentation bombs sat in the hold, each designed to knock out utilities and crater the roads. Their sole purpose was to make the second wave's job easier – the second wave, following shortly behind in formation, were carrying incendiaries − magnesium or petroleum.

With cratered roads and the water supply gone, fire engines would struggle to get to and extinguish the fires these bombs would create.

Oswald's job at this stage was simply to keep his nerve. He could feel the sweat on his gloved palms as he held the joystick steady, levelling their approach. Hearing a barely masked whimper, he looked over his shoulder at Gunter. Their eyes met, and Oswald recognised the fear in them. The freckle-faced gunner visibly shook with each explosion that rattled the hull of their bomber.

"Remember your training, Kuhne – Gunter. The enemy's guns bark, but rarely bite."

Karl interjected, placing a comforting hand on Gunter's shoulder, before quoting from his favourite playwright. It was one of the few compassionate things Oswald had ever seen from Karl.

"It is a tale told by an idiot, full of sound and fury, signifying nothing."

Wilhelm, smiling as a thought occurred to him, turned from his gunner's seat to look at Karl. "Quoting Shakespeare, Karl? Isn't he from this neck of the woods? You might end up accidentally bombing his house."

"He's pretty far from here, Wilhelm. Stratford-upon-Avon. Our bombs are neither that powerful, nor that inaccurate."

"Speaking of which," shouted Oswald, the flares of their markers now visible on the rapidly approaching horizon. The men instantly fell silent, each with a job to do.

*

He wasn't counting, but Thomas "Tommo" Watson, in his small half-hour shift manning the anti-aircraft cannon, fired nearly six hundred shells. He'd never see the one that hit, the explosion from the bomber lost in all the other eruptions filling both sky and land.

But if we were lucky enough to see it, that grey projectile, the silver tip glinting in the moonlight. If we were gifted enough to follow its trajectory, we would observe its predecessor falling inches short. The same would happen to the shell that followed, but this one – one of many shots that night fired in frustration - would strike true.

Tommo would never know this. The result would make the pages of a few history books, but Thomas would never trouble those same pages, not even as a footnote. His War story ends here. He'll feature heavily in the stories of his wife, children, and grandchildren, but that needn't concern us. We have more pressing matters.

*

The best part of the evening having been filled with them, it was easy to become immune to the sound of explosions, to block them out as white background noise. But not this one.

An eruption from right outside the plane, a white-hot phosphorous burst like a flash of lightning. The bomber jolted in the air, dramatically veering to the left as the familiar and comforting drone of the two working propellers became halved.

For every light that started flashing on their instrumentation, another switched off, never to reignite.

Wilhelm craned his neck from his gunner's position to stare at their right wing – or what remained of their right wing. "The wing's shredded," he shouted, staring at the smouldering, red-hot metal edges of where their right propeller had been.

Oswald grimaced, struggling to right the protesting Dornier. It took every ounce of his strength to level the plane, the controls sluggish to respond.

"We're losing fuel too," said Gunter, tapping the gauge. They turned to see it pouring from the wing, the metal bird's life-giving ichor draining from it with every passing moment.

"Scheiße," spat Oswald, thumping the controls, "We're going to have to abort. Jettison the payload."

There was a justified panic in all their voices, but a calm contemplation too. They had been trained for this, and even Gunter, poor terrified Gunter, was determined not to let his fellow airmen down.

Karl turned the first of the bomb release levers to drop the first deadly payload. They could hear the grinding of metal behind and below them, and it took all his strength for those final few turns.

"First payload away," he barked, already sensing that the last of their luck had just left them.

His intuition was correct; the second lever refused to turn, telling him all he needed to know. All the strength in the world wouldn't open the inevitable tangle of twisted metal hatch mechanism that prevented the remainder of the bombs from falling.

"The Bomb release mechanism is gebrochen. Means we've still got eight SC50's in the hold."

"It gets worse, gentlemen," said Oswald, his attention turning back to his controls, "The wing is on fire. And the fuel with it."

Gunter turned to look at the wing. Despite the rising heat in the cockpit, his blood chilled at the sight. Most of the wing was now on fire, a deadly conflagration that was spreading. The fuel that spilled from it fell as flashing bolts of lightning, sparking and igniting.

"We have to bail out!" he screamed, desperately trying to make eye contact with one of his companions. Oswald turned to face him, glaring.

"If you panic, Gunter, we all die. Karl, keep trying that release valve. Give Gunter your maps."

Karl handed the folder of maps to Gunter's quivering hands. He understood. Keeping the boy busy was a means of keeping him from panicking further.

Oswald leaned in closer to the panicked man, now reduced to trembling boy. "Find us a runway. Somewhere we can land this dying bird."

Gunter nodded, turning his attention to the array of maps and reconnaissance photographs that filled the bulky cardboard folder stamped with the black eagle stencil of the Luftwaffe. The sweat that poured from his brow stung at his eyes, blurring the numbers and letters into illegible chaos. Concentrate, man...

"Found one!" he announced, triumphantly, "RAF Wymeswold. Bearing zero three five. Sixty-six kilometres."

"Last chance for that bomb release, Karl!" shouted Oswald, glancing behind him. Karl, as predicted, shook his head.

Muttering to himself, the pilot yanked on the joystick, guiding their stricken vessel away from the other bombers. The drone of propellers faded, replaced by the unsteady sound of their own craft, engines sputtering and fading, pushed to their operational limits.

Wilhelm, who had remained mostly silent as he'd made peace with his God, stared at the darkness ahead of them. Somewhere in that spattering of lights was an airfield and their potential salvation. "I hear the RAF torture their prisoners," he said, the fear apparent in his tone.

"They probably say the same about us, Wilhelm," said Gunter, calmer now.

"Only they'd be right," muttered Karl, remembering the precise moment that had stolen his faith.

*

Optimism is a double-edged sword. It can be a blessing, keeping you soldiering on when you'd otherwise have long since quit, but it can also be cruelly snatched away.

They all smelt the fuel at the same time, felt the heat within the cockpit increasing. Karl, familiar with every inch of this aircraft, also knew what it was. He'd kept quiet to keep everyone's spirits buoyant, wondering in all honesty how they'd kept in the air so long. Perhaps Wilhelm's God was with them after all, just not the whole of the way.

It would have been a miracle if the same blast that had irreparably damaged one of the bomb doors hadn't damaged the fuel tanks back there as well, and it was only a matter of time until a spark from the wing ended up in there.

Gunter was mercifully killed instantly by the huge blast that erupted from behind, his blackened corpse only kept in his chair by a thin sliver of smouldering seat belt. Karl was not so lucky, caught in the periphery of the explosion and on the edge of the firestorm, pierced by a dozen white hot metal fragments. As he lay there dying, agony overwhelming every sense, he stared through the hole in the plane's hull at the starless sky and sentinel moon. Closing his eyes, he went to join them.

Oswald and Wilhelm, seated in the front, had been shielded from most of the explosion by their unlucky colleagues, but the fire did not discriminate. It leapt from wall to floor to ceiling, ever approaching.

"We need to bail out!" screamed Wilhelm, his seat belt already undone.

Oswald looked at him, the beads of sweat on his forehead illuminated in the creeping orange glow. He looked calm, resigned to his fate. "Not me, Will."

Wilhelm placed a hand on the pilot's shoulder, urging him to get up.

Oswald placed both hands on the joystick, wrenching it back to level the protesting plane. He looked to his colleague, now forced to shout over the whipping of wind from outside, the grinding of metal and the roaring flames.

"We are far from Coventry now, Will. These are houses below us, civilians. We are a flying bomb, and I cannot doom these people to that fate. You go – I need to find somewhere safe to bring us down."

The young gunner nodded, understanding. There would be no landing. Oblivious to the flames that now lapped at their chairs, at the instruments around them, he sat back down.

Visibility was non-existent, both front windows a tight spiders web of thick cracks. It was barely possible to differentiate land from sky.

"So be it. If tonight we meet God," Wilhelm said, resigned now to his fate, "let at least our consciences be a little clearer."

*

A witness, a local farmer, saw the damaged flight's final moments. The plane was flying so low, he could see the crew's faces. With an engine ablaze, the cockpit was aglow with flame, but the farmer swore blind that the pilot looked at him, but this sounds fanciful at best; an already entertaining anecdote given unnecessary flavour.

*

In the stricken Dornier's final moments, it struggled to clear a row of Poplar trees. Striking them, the flaming pyre that had once been Luftwaffe 2892 BK+BP crashed and burned through the thick foliage, eventually coming to a halt in the grounds of Prestwold Hall, near Loughborough. It burned throughout the night and much of the next morning, and eight unexploded SC50kg bombs were found in the smouldering wreckage.

There is a curious honour amongst pilots, a mutual respect between those men brave – or foolhardy enough to launch themselves into enemy skies. In a funeral organised by the RAF, a procession carried the four coffins through Loughborough before a private ceremony at Loughborough Cemetery. Many lined the streets to pay their respects. There was no shouting or jeering, no gloating over an enemy come to an end. The four Luftwaffe airmen were buried with full military honours.

Their graves are still there, well maintained, fresh flowers regularly left upon them. Each slate-white grave is adorned with the symbol of the Iron Cross.

LESSONS IN HOW TO QUEUE

By Emilie Lauren Jones

Inspired by true events at an unnamed gym in Coventry

I think I should go first, don't you?
I had been considering which overpriced oatcake
to choose as you slipped into the half space
in front of me.

My stuttering reply dies as you repeat:
I think I should go first.
I nod.
You should go first.

You should go first because
you pay a monthly direct debit to this gym
instead of using a free guest pass you picked
up in the community centre raffle.

You should go first because
the woman serving has smiled at you from across
this counter for over two years and her daughter
looks a bit like your daughter.

You should go first because
you are branded with designer sweat bands
and own a keyless car that you remember to vacuum
before it looks like it needs it.

You should go first because
when you call your dog's name in the park
he comes back to you instead of digging up
the kids play area.

You should go first because
you know they're 'gilets' not 'bodywarmers',
you can spell 'pretentious' without having to Google it
and can bake banana cake without looking at the recipe.

You should go first because
you got married on a sunny day with a brass band
and honeymooned in Cape Verde instead of mistaking
it for a type of pasta at a pub quiz.

You should go first because
you remembered to wear a blue dress on polling day
and you've never got changed in a train toilet or come
home looking like that girl from the DrinkAware advert.

You should go first because
you have lavender liners in your underwear drawer,
and your nasal passages recognise the floral tones of Dior
but have yet to experience Oxfam's washing powder.

You should go first because
shops sell keyrings with your name on them
and people pronounce it without assistance
and the man at Starbucks writes it correctly on your cup.

You should go first because
you know Manet did portraits and Monet did flowers,
you know which knife to use first at dinner parties
and that people who get stopped by police must deserve it.

You should go first because
you had skiing lessons when you were six
and ever since, you've known that life's
a bespoke slide for you to traverse.

You should go first because
when the others in this queue look between me
and you, they already know all of these things.
They know who goes first.

SKY BLUE RAINBOW RIPPLES

By Ella Cook

Elisa was glad there wasn't anyone around. She was more than aware that she probably looked more than a little nuts as she skipped and hopped around the park's flower beds, humming as she worked. That was part of the reason she always started so early: that and there was something so magical about the early winter mornings that it seemed appropriate to her work to be there just as the sun fought her way over the frosty horizon.

Still humming, Elisa tucked her long skirts between her knees so she could kneel down and nestle another magical splodge of colour into the cold dirt. First, she found her spot and dug a small hole, before dropping her rainbow treasure into place and patting the soil carefully around it, making sure it was secure.

She wasn't wearing the ideal clothes for gardening – but when even the weather was dull and grey and cold, she couldn't bear the thought of drab clothes too. She needed all the colour and joy she could find. So today, her skirt was dark green, over equally green tights, and topped with a bright yellow jumper beneath her purple coat. If it was good enough for the crocuses and daffodils peeking through the cold earth, it would be good enough for her, she reasoned.

Her hair fell across her face, fighting its way free to curl against her cheek, and she shoved the purple strands back under her woollen hat – hand crocheted in all her favourite colours by her favourite aunt – before tucking another treasure into the dark earth.

It wasn't something everyone would do, but it was a part of her job that she enjoyed, and since she'd started the tradition five years ago, she couldn't contemplate not doing it. Even though her work went unnoticed by most of the world, it would mean a lot to those few special people who did see it.

It was a long job, and if she were honest the heavy bag and constant bending made her back ache a little – but it would be worth it to see the reactions of the local community. Last year, people from all over Coventry and Warwickshire had flooded into Allesley Park to view her work, musing and questioning where her treasures had come from, what they'd meant, and how they'd got there. Much to her amusement, she'd even trended briefly on social media and had been featured in local papers.

And this time, with so many children and older people involved from all around the city, she was expecting it to be bigger than ever, with parks in Longford, Holbrooks, and Radford receiving similar treatment from her co-conspirators. It was going to be the best year yet!

*

Trevor slammed the drawer shut and flung his snack bars and favourite pen into the box that already contained his mug, spare tie, deodorant, and the tacky desk-top golf set that his Secret Santa had delivered just a few weeks ago. Things had seemed so much brighter then, fuelled by alcohol, only-slightly-forced festive cheer, and the hope of the new year.

What really, really stung and rankled was the fact that the management team had known about the redundancies at the same time that they'd been planning the lavish Christmas party. But like so many print media organisations, his company were down-sizing. Which was a polite way of saying his career was lying in the dust after a solid, pink-slip shaped knockout blow.

He shook his head again, angered by the unfairness of it all. For years, he'd worked in the community, tracking down stories that would be of interest to the diverse mix of cultures and people that made up modern-day Coventry. He'd covered everything from the Sky Blue's rise and falls to the annual Godiva festival, to Time Team's excavation of Roman ruins and the arrival – and closure of the initially controversial and then loved and hated Ikea.

And now he was redundant. Superfluous to requirements. Unneeded, unwanted, and unemployed. And unclear about what he was supposed to do with his future. He'd get a little bit of redundancy payment, but nowhere near enough to live on long-term, and certainly not enough to cover the ongoing mortgage on his Allesley home. It broke his heart to think of selling the cottage. It was only a little two-bed, but it had history and he'd spent many a happy weekend lovingly turning it from the derelict, uncared for wreck he'd purchased into the cosy home it now was.

He'd fought hard to keep his little house in the divorce, and he'd thrown himself into his work – often putting in fifty hours a week – and now it seemed that all that effort was going to go to waste. He snatched the box from what used to be his desk and stomped out of what used to be his office, nearly ruining the effect by stumbling on the raised bit of carpet he wouldn't miss at all; and left the newspaper that used to be his employer, wondering what he was going to do with himself as he left what used to be his life behind.

*

Elisa drew out the last-but-one of her secrets and stretched up on her tiptoes to tie it onto a tree branch, then re-arranged the leaves so that it was mostly hidden. She didn't want to make them too easy to find – if they were found with no effort, then some of the magic was lost.

She rubbed the small of her back and rolled her head on her shoulders. It had been a long few hours and she was tired, but she'd almost finished. Just one left in this batch, and then she'd treat herself to a hot coffee, and probably a slice of cake. Surely bobbing up and down countless dozens of times was at least as good as a spin class at the gym?

She looked around, partly to decide where to place it, and partly to make sure she was still alone. She didn't want to be caught now, not when she was so close to finishing and perfecting everything.

After a final check, she knelt down and tucked her final package in between the roots of the tree and gently rearranged some of the daffodil fronds to partly cover it. She dusted off her hands, pleased with her work, but just as she was about to straighten up, a well-pressed suit slammed into her, and for a moment she was as airborne as one of the garden's fairies.

Strong hands grabbed at her as a heavy, pointed shadow collided with her temple. It knocked the sense from her and ended her brief flight – leaving her teetering as metaphorical cartoon birds joined the stars spinning in her vision.

"Bugger. I'm so sorry, are you alright?" Even upside down, and obscured by the twittering birds and stars, her rescuer/attacker was attractive.

"I think so." Elisa winced as she was returned to her feet, gingerly touched her fingers to the throbbing spot on her head and pulled away sticky fingers.

"Crap! You're bleeding. I'm so, so, sorry. Should I call an ambulance or something?" His phone was already in his hand.

"No, I'm fine." Elisa shook her head, and instantly regretted the movement as the stars returned. "Actually, I am a little dizzy. Maybe you could help me to a bench."

"Of course." A strong arm slipped beneath hers, offering comfort and support against her wobbly knees, pulling her back to the path. A few dozen steps later, and she was seated on a bench, the cold seeping through her layers to make her shiver.

"Will you be alright for a moment?" Kind, dark eyes peered at her with concern from beneath a thatch of fuzzy looking black hair as he produced a clean-looking handkerchief from his pocket and handed it to her.

"I'll be fine, thank you." Elisa was already mentally reviewing her mandatory first aid training: she hadn't lost consciousness, so should be fine to head home and warm up in the bubble bath that she really felt she deserved. Cake could wait. Or she could combine the two…

"You won't try to move?" he persisted.

"I won't move." If she was honest, she was still feeling a little shaky, and was probably best to not move for a few minutes. She almost definitely needed the comforting sweetness of cake.

"OK." He nodded, then jogged back to where she'd taken flight and started scooping things off the ground. She pressed the crisp white cotton handkerchief to her aching temple, watching him as she wondered what his story was. It wasn't most men his age who still carried around hankies, ready to hand them over to damsels in distress after assaulting them.

*

Trevor dumped the escapee items back into their box, then tucked it under his arm and headed back to where the woman he'd inadvertently attacked was perched on the bench. He walked back slowly, taking his time to calm his breathing and study her. The last thing he needed now was to be yelled at – or sued – for hurting her. She didn't seem too upset, but she was bleeding slightly, and he had knocked her hard.

Something told him she wasn't going to go down that route, but you never could tell how strangers would react, or what they'd do. He shook his head. Sometimes, you couldn't even tell what people you'd worked alongside for years were really going to do.

Looking at her now, sitting uncomfortably on the bench with her head resting in her hands, he wondered how he could possibly have missed her. She was dressed like a cartoon character or escapee children's TV presenter. There was so much colour in her outfit that she seemed to glow against the dull, cold day, and despite everything he couldn't help a small smile at the sight of her.

"I really am very sorry." He approached the bench slowly, unsure of what he should do.

"It was an accident." She shrugged. "They happen. It's not like you launched me into the air and attacked me with your box on purpose, is it?"

"No, of course not."

"Then it's no harm done." She stood up, but instantly grabbed for the arm of the bench, wobbling slightly as the cartoon birds whistled in her head, threatening to return.

Trevor grabbed her arm, steadying her to sit again. "Are you sure you don't want me to call for help?"

"No, I'm really fine."

"Can I at least walk you to wherever you were going, and make sure you're really alright?" He was worried about her dizziness, and how she'd started to shiver.

"Actually, I was just about finished. My car is back in the village."

Shit. He couldn't let her drive. What if she passed out behind the wheel? "You know, there's a nice pub in the village. Maybe I could buy you a cup of tea, and you could warm up, and make sure you're alright before you drive. If nothing else, they'll have a first aid kit. Where exactly is your car?"

"In Butcher's Lane, just up from..."

"The Rainbow Inn," he finished for her. "The pub I was going to suggest. Do you think you can walk there?" He eyed her with concern.

"I'm fine just sitting here," she argued.

"Well, I'm cold, and I can't imagine you're not." He glanced at her quivering knees that were causing her long skirt to jump and dance. He tucked the box containing the detritus of his entire career under one arm and held out his other hand to her. "I'm Trevor."

"Elisa." She placed a hand that was, unsurprisingly to Trevor, wrapped in a colourful hand warmer from which pale fingers topped off by bright blue nails emerged. Trying not to smile at the contrast of her delicate, brightly coloured hand in his, he gently tugged, pulling her to her feet. As she stood, he held onto her, making sure she didn't stumble or waiver again. But instead of swaying, she gave him a bright smile and tucked her hand into the crook of his elbow, and followed his lead to the pub.

*

"So, asides from knocking people down and assaulting them with heavy boxes, what's your link with Allesley park, if you don't mind me asking?" Elisa unwound her scarf, stripped off her colourful gloves and rested them on the edge of the table. Though she'd been past the pub a number of times, it was almost always when she'd been working, and somehow, she'd never quite managed to make it inside. Looking around the cosy pub, with its ancient beams and flagstones that had probably been polished smooth by countless thousands of feet over hundreds of years, she regretted having not visited before.

"It's fine." Trevor couldn't see any reason not to tell her. "I live here. I've got a little cottage in the village."

"One of the old ones?"

"Complete with a thatched roof." He grinned proudly.

"I always think they look like something out of a fairy tale. You're so lucky."

"Yes." He nodded, thinking he was going to need every bit of luck possible to keep hold of it now he was unemployed. He tried to shake off the thought and focussed on her instead. "What about you? Do you live in Allesley?"

"No," she laughed. "It's a bit rich for my pocket. I'm just visiting for work."

Trevor gave her a strange look. "Are you a gardener of some sort?"

"No." Elisa smiled. "And if I were, I'd probably wear wellies instead of heels. And something more sensible than this."

"Well… I didn't like to say anything, as we've only just met."

"It's not like we're total strangers," Elisa grinned. "It's not just anyone who manages to knock me off my feet."

"I still can't apologise enough. Though I'm still not sure how I missed seeing you."

"You probably weren't expecting to see anyone on their hands and knees half under a tree."

"Especially someone who I now know isn't a gardener."

"Exactly." She wove her fingers around her steaming cup and answered his silent question. "I'm a social worker."

"So, what were you doing in the park?"

"Just a work project. How about you? What do you do when you're not hanging around the park?"

"I'm a journalist… or at least, I was. This…" he pointed to the offending box. "is basically what's left of my career. I got made redundant today."

"Oh, I'm so sorry to hear that!" Elisa automatically reached out a comforting hand.

"Thanks," he sighed. "It's been coming for a while. There were layoffs last year, and talk of more, but we had a good Christmas and I'd let myself believe that maybe I was safe… that it was over. But sadly, I was wrong. And now I have to figure out what to do next."

"Could you try freelancing?"

"Maybe. But it's a pretty competitive market. Apparently, there weren't even enough good stories to keep me in normal employment, and at least there I wasn't competing for copy space. And it's hard enough to get some people to talk to you even when you're affiliated with a paper. I can't imagine it's going to suddenly get easier now. And with no story, there's not really any work."

Elisa pursed her lips and fiddled with the stone that had been a comforting weight in her pocket for over six years now. She'd worked hard to preserve the secrecy around her project, but maybe there was a way that the magic could continue without the secrecy? Perhaps the truth – now it was so successful, could make things even better? And could she really justify keeping her secret now, when it might help someone? The whole reason she'd started her project was to help people, and though she'd never planned on helping people on a face-to-face basis, she couldn't help feeling that maybe fate had put them together today – or more accurately, put her slap bang in the middle of his pathway. And she'd always been a big believer in fate...

After a few more moments of internal debate, she slowly pulled the rainbow chiffon bag out of her pocket, and carefully tipped the small stone into her palm. It was only about two inches across, and the front was painted with a slightly clumsy, but still beautiful rainbow which shone out from beneath the slight gloss that was doubtless the result of a layer of varnish similar to the ones she used on every creation.

She placed it in Trevor's hand, knowing that when he turned it over, he'd see the words 'Don't Give Up, Your Dreams are in Reach!' inked onto the back.

"It's a nice idea." He studied the writing, and then sighed. "If only it was that easy."

40

"Maybe there could be a story in that." Elisa pointed to the stone, before adding carefully. "I think I've seen quite a bit of speculation about them over the last few years."

"You're right. I wrote a couple of articles last year." His fingers traced over the rainbow, following the different colours as they curved across the smooth, grey stone. "No one knows where they come from, or why they're there. But people travel from all over the city, and even further sometimes, to hunt for them and follow the fairy trails."

"So, you think there's still interest in them?"

"Maybe," he shrugged. "I've heard it's spreading and there are other areas doing similar things, but I think ours were some of the first. Certainly, the first in the Midlands. But the mystery hasn't been solved in the last few years. I don't think it's going to be any time soon.'

"This is being done in other areas? The stones?" She tried not to let her huge grin of pride escape and give her away too soon.

"Yeah. And the toadstools and fairy doors and houses and stuff."

"So, finding out where they come from might be a story? One you could sell?"

"Probably. Almost definitely, depending on the back story.' His eyes narrowed as he watched her. 'You know, don't you?'

"Maybe." Elisa grinned and leaned forward. "I was a mature student by the time I decided I wanted to become a social worker. There were times it was... difficult being one of the older people in the room. I had a lot more responsibilities and stresses – like my house payments – than the kids who'd gone straight from college into uni. My placement year was especially hard."

"I can understand that."

"I got close to dropping out in my final year – just around Easter. My sister found that stone on holiday in Massachusetts and brought it back for me. She said she'd been wondering how she could help me, and nearly tripped over it – so obviously it was meant for me. It's been living in my pocket most of the years since."

"And you didn't drop out?"

"Nope, I finished the degree – including the placement year, and got a job with the city council."

"And you're saying the stone did all that?"

Elisa shrugged. "I know it sounds a little silly, that a hand-painted pebble could change so much, but it made me smile and think for a few moments that maybe things weren't so bad, and after that it was like ripples in a still pond: it became like a talisman for good luck and things seemed to go right more often."

"And...?"

"And the next year, I wanted to share that positivity and magic. So, I made some of my own, and hid them around the park. And people seemed to like them, so the next year I got some of the kids I work with, and some of my family and friends, to help. And this year has been even more special."

"How?"

"This year a relative – my aunt – and her friends have gotten involved too, crocheting and knitting little gifts and toys like flowers, and hearts, and these." She pulled a tiny, crocheted bird out of her pocket and placed it on his palm. 'We're going to hang them in trees."

"Wow!" He stared at the perfectly formed little creature that wasn't even as big as his thumb and flipped over the brightly coloured label and read it aloud, *'I'm not lost, just hanging around alone, if I've made you smile, please feel free to take me home.'* That's brilliant."

"We've held craft groups where some of our children have learned how to make things like this, taught by some of our older community members. It's been amazing. The kids are loving it, and it's almost turned into a foster grandparent scheme.'

"That's amazing."

"It's been brilliant." Her eyes were alight with passion as she spoke, and he found it easy to understand how she'd achieved so much. He found himself wanting to volunteer to help despite not being the least bit crafty.

"So, you've been behind it all?" He leaned forward, his voice low. "The coloured pebbles, the toadstools...?"

"And fairy doors, footsteps and acorn trails. Yes, with a lot of help," Elisa nodded.

"But you've never told anyone?"

"Nope. Everyone involved is sworn to secrecy."

"Why?"

"Because the magic is important. When you throw a penny in a wishing well, or blow out birthday candles, you don't tell people what your wish is, do you?" She waited for him to shake his head. "Well, it's a bit like that. The pebbles, and their messages, are a bit like wishes or prayers. They're messages of hope. Every single one of them is someone taking time and energy and effort to put something positive and good into the world. And for some of the children I work with – who haven't had much good in their worlds – that's incredibly powerful. It is a type of magic, and I didn't want that spell to be broken."

Trevor nodded in understanding. "When you put it like that, it is pretty magical. So why are you speaking out now? Why are you telling me?"

He watched as she took a deep breath and reached for the rainbow stone. "Because maybe you should turn this into your first freelance story. You said yourself that it's probably of interest. Do you still think so?"

"Yes," he nodded earnestly. "Even more so with your story behind it and knowing about the children you've got involved. And I love the idea of foster grandparents."

"Then you should write the story."

"Are you sure?" Even though he'd only just met her, he felt protective of Elisa and didn't want to push her into doing something she might regret – no matter how much he really, really wanted this story.

"Yes." She nodded slowly. "I think maybe this story – mine, and the kids' and our foster grannies' – maybe it's your rainbow stone?' She laughed. 'And technically, you did catch me in the act. So the secret's out."

"That would be amazing." Trevor felt a huge grin spreading across his face, already thinking about the different editors he could potentially sell it to. "Are you sure?"

Elisa nodded again. "I am. But don't think you're getting this for free."

Crap! He might have known there would be a catch. "I've just been made redundant. And even if I hadn't, I wouldn't really have a budget for something like this."

Elisa laughed, surprising him. "I don't want your money. I want your help. I've got a shopping bag full of these..." she pointed to the little bird still nestled in his palm, "and you're going to help me hang them."

"How can you be so sure?" He fought to supress a grin, already knowing he was going to help however he could.

"Well," she shrugged. "It's not like you've got anywhere else to be, is it?" She rested her fingers against his, just next to the little woollen bird. "What do you say? Want to help me start some more ripples?"

He looked down at the bright blue nails and gave in to the grin. "Sky Blue ripples?"

"Nah." Elisa grinned at him, making him feel like there might be light and hope in the world again. "Blue's just one colour – however pretty. I'm planning a whole rainbow."

"Sky blue rainbow ripples?" Trevor mused. "There might just be something in that." He reached into his box for a notepad, and after the few seconds of seemingly wearing out what little patience she had, Elisa tugged at his hand.

"Come on. We've got to hang this bird and all his friends somewhere, and I need you for the taller branches!"

*

Across the city, the laughter of a child echoed through Longford park. "Higher, Daddy! Higher!' Chubby fingers wrapped around carefully formed yarn and tugged a few times before a triumphant cry filled the air.

"What do you have there?"

"It's a little fairy, and she's dressed like a flower. She's so pretty. Can I keep her? Please?"

The man studied the tiny, purple-haired knitted doll, and tugged at the tag attached to the ribbon that had held her aloft. He smiled, then read it to his *daughter 'I'm a random act of kindness, not lost - just alone. Will you be my friend? Do you want to take me home?'*

"Yes please!" The little fingers tugged at the flower fairy and hugged her against the fuzzy coat the little girl wore against the cold. "I think I'll call her Daffodil. Do you like it?"

"She does look at bit like a daffodil," her dad mused, while wondering where the magical little gift had come from. Wherever it was, he was grateful. It was the first time he'd seen his little girl smile so much since they'd moved to the city a few weeks ago.

BEST APP EVER

By Bev Woodley

It's me. Charlie. I'm recording this on my iPad. I think I've turned the internet settings off. Not sure. I don't want this – this *thing* networking onto anyone else's phone or social media. It can't go viral!

They check phones and iPads don't they? I'm sure they always check stuff like phones and computers when someone goes missing. Yeah, they do. Well, they do on TV police programmes. The ones Mum likes. That's why I'm recording this. In case it gets me too.

Today, started like any normal Sunday afternoon. House to myself. Mum at work. Early lunch, so Dad could take my pain-in-the-neck baby sister to her dance classes...

The front doorbell chimed. "Hi, Tyrone," I said as I opened our door.

"Charlie, you're not going to believe it!" My best mate's grin disappeared from view as he hoisted a cardboard box right up in my face. "I know what the clue means. I found Fantasy Fest! Want a game?"

"You're joking. That clue was only posted yesterday!"

I remembered how excited we'd both been when we found the clue: *Fantasy Fest – the best app ever, can only be found if you are clever.*

In Albion's middle, look in Coffa's Tree.

The chamber is 'Silence' – the gadgets are free!

Tyrone was convinced it was in Coventry. His Dad was into local history and stuff like that. That's how Tyrone knew that some historians believe Coventry was originally called, Coffa's Tree. But try as we might, we couldn't work out the last bit. All I could

47

think of was Harry Potter, but that was the *Chamber of Secrets* - not the *Chamber of Silence.*

"You've never found the Chamber of Silence!"

"I did. Talk about jammy," Tyrone said as he walked into the lounge and dumped the box on the coffee table.

"Dad insisted we all go to the Memorial Park for Remembrance Sunday. Promised to drop me off at yours after. Anyway, Dad got mad 'cos I was gazing at my phone during the minute's silence. After the service, he demanded to know what I was playing. I told him I wasn't playing anything and showed him the Fantasy Fest clue."

"And he knew what it meant?"

"Yeah. He said there's a room inside the War Memorial. Who knew? I didn't. Anyway, it's open to the public once a year – on Remembrance Sunday!"

"What's that got to do with the app?"

"Get this. The room's called – drum roll please – the Chamber of Silence!"

"Nooo!"

"Yeah. Dad and I went in. While Dad was viewing the Roll of the Fallen, I started looking around the chamber."

"...and that's where you found the box?"

"Not exactly. I'd looked everywhere and couldn't find a thing. So, I wandered round again. This time looking up. Y'know, in case something was hung from the ceiling."

"...and it was?"

"Nope, but 'cos I was looking up, I bumped into a weird man. He reminded me of Yoda in Star Wars. No, Dobby. He was more like Dobby the house elf. His beige anorak certainly looked like the oversized thing Dobby wears – except his had sleeves. The man, not Dobby. Thinking about it now, he appeared out of nowhere too. Just like Dobby. Anyway, before I could say, 'Sorry' for bumping into him, he shoved this box into my hands and shuffled off."

The box, which now sat on our coffee table, had a label on it which read:

CONGRATULATIONS!

YOU NOW OWN FANTASY FEST – THE BEST APP EVER!

"...and he just gave it to you? Just like that?"

"Yeah. Probably chose me because I was at least forty years younger than anyone else in the room."

"Hmm, I guess he must work for the company. Tyrone, you're so jammy."

"I know!" Grinning, Tyrone knelt to pull the tape off the box. "Come on mate, let's see what's in here."

White polystyrene blobs fell to the floor as I helped Tyrone clear away the packaging and pull out the contents. Best lucky-dip ever! It felt like Christmas. It even looked like it'd snowed inside. We found a voucher and two Virtual Reality (VR) goggles for 'total immersion' in the game. Tyrone grabbed the voucher. I scooped the fake snow back into the empty box and stuffed it behind the sofa.

"Hey, the code to download the app for free works for two people. Charlie, you can get the app for free too."

"Sick! Does that mean we can only play the app with each other?"

"Hold on. Nope, if you've downloaded the full app you can play with anyone on your contacts list. Oh, but they do need the VR goggles."

"Okay. I'm gonna get a drink while you download the app," I said. "Want one?"

"Got any juice?"

"I think we've got apple."

"Great. I'll have that."

I dashed to the kitchen, grabbed a couple of glasses and was pouring the apple juice when Tyrone shouted, "Charlie! Is your Bluetooth turned on?"

"Should be," I said as I walked back in the room with our drinks. "Why?"

"If I select 'two players' the app searches for the nearest Bluetooth to link to."

"Don't select it yet. I need to check my phone. I'll be gutted if you end up playing Fantasy Fest with Mrs Patel next door!" I snatched up my phone. "Go ahead. It's on."

"OK. I've selected the 'two-player' option. Look…" Tyrone placed his phone into the VR goggles with the screen facing towards him, "…when you get the app, slot your phone in the other VR goggles. See how my screen says, 'Player One'?"

"I've got the app now," I said and tapped to open it. "Wow, it says, 'Player Two'."

"Great, I'm a Knight. What about you?"

"Err…" I swiped the screen looking at all the options. There was no point being a dwarf if Tyrone was a knight – their strengths and weaknesses were too similar. No, I needed a character with a bit of magic. Only thing was I didn't like the look of the gnomes, brownies or elves. "Got it. I'll be a wizard."

"Great, let's play!" Tyrone tapped the 'Player One confirm' button and put the goggles on.

Lining up my phone I rammed it into the other VR goggles. Up popped the 'Player Two confirm' button and I tapped it. On my screen an image of Tyrone appeared dressed as a knight. His silver armour glowed like moonlight. The visor on his helmet was up, displaying his midnight face – lit by a familiar grin which shone almost as bright as his metal casing.

"Wow! The graphics are fantastic. That looks just like you!" I exclaimed, turning to Tyrone – or where Tyrone should have been.

There was a slight indentation in the sofa, but no Tyrone. Nothing was there. Not Tyrone. Not the goggles. Not his phone. Nothing to show he'd ever been here.

No, there was something. Something very faint in the background. It was coming from my phone. I lifted the VR goggles. Tyrone's voice was coming from my phone,

"Hurry up, Charlie! I can't move until you join me. It's amazing, mate. It's like I'm really here."

"Y-you are."

"What did you say? I can't hear you. Speak into the microphone. Y'know, on the goggles."

"Tyrone," I shouted. No way was I putting the VR goggles on until I knew what had happened to my mate. "You're not here. You're in the game."

"I know. It's fantastic!"

"Y-your body, Tyrone! It's not on the sofa next to me. You've disappeared!"

"What? But…"

"Take the VR goggles off. Now!"

Tyrone's hands rose towards his head and tugged off the knight's helmet. He didn't reappear on the sofa. On-screen an arrow flew through the air, missing Tyrone-the-Knight's face by millimetres. More arrows rushed towards him.

"Put your helmet back on!" I screamed down the microphone.

As soon as Tyrone's helmet was in place the arrows stopped.

"Did you see who was shooting at you?"

"N-no. Every direction I look there's a grey wall saying, 'Level locked.' All except when I look straight ahead... Charlie, I'm not sure I like this anymore."

"I'll get you out, Mate. Just let me think."

"You won't. When I look straight ahead, there's a door saying, 'Awaiting player two to begin first level.' That's you, Charlie. I won't let you get stuck in here too. Stay out. Stay out and try and get me out."

*

"Mum. Dad, if you're watching this, I love you, but you do understand, don't you? I've read, I've re-read the instructions. I've tried everything. Nothing works. I can't leave Tyrone. The App's set up as a two-player game. Without me he's stuck, maybe forever. I can't abandon him.

I'm leaving my iPad plugged in and recording. In case, well, in case I disappear too. Perhaps it's like that film, *Jumanji*. Y'know, if we complete all the levels we get to go home. If not HELP US! Restore to default settings or, I don't know, try anything. Just get us home."

*

On the iPad's screen, Charlie's hand trembles a little as he picks up the VR goggles. His hazel eyes disappear behind the VR goggles. The iPad displays an empty leather sofa, slightly indented with a Charlie-sized seat. The only on-screen movement, a lone fly buzzing between two undrunk glasses of apple juice.

*

"Charlie!" Dad stomps around the house. "Where's that boy got to now? Grace, have you seen your brother?"

"He's not in here," replies Grace turning off her brother's iPad and walking out of the lounge. "I'm going up to my bedroom."

Pain-in-the-neck, am I? I'll show you Charlie! Now, where can I hide his iPad so Mum and Dad won't find it?

FRIDAY NIGHT AT THE GOLDEN CROSS

By Maxine Burns

Everyone knows I like a pint or six on a Friday night. I've been coming here for years to meet my pals, have a laugh and relax after the week's work.

I expect you've heard of the Golden Cross, it being one of the oldest bars in Coventry. It's not the easiest pub to find, tucked away at the top of a narrow, cobbled street, next to the old, decaying assizes. To the rear is the site of the last public hanging of a woman, who was buried standing up, reportedly in the Inn's own grounds. Unsurprisingly, it has the reputation of being one of the most haunted pubs in Warwickshire, although I must say, the only spirits I've seen are in the optics behind the bar.

I imagine you're thinking that this is going to be a tall tale from a cynic who, at the end declares his conversion to the dark arts after a ghostly experience in the gents. Well, you would be wrong. I'm just an ordinary bloke who has never seen anything remotely spooky and never expects to.

The bar was hazy tonight as I walked through the door and it took a minute for my eyes to adjust before I saw the gang, sitting at our usual table, laughing, drinking pints, or knocking back whisky chasers. Making my way over, I pulled up a chair, sat and leaned back looking around the room, smiling, waiting for a gap in the conversation to enable me to join in. My smile slipped a little as I glanced from face to face. Jed had grown a beard and Mike had put on a lot of weight. Well, that wasn't right, not in a week, surely?

Andy was sitting beside me. We go way back, right from junior school. We've both been married and divorced, and we live in the same street, we practically share a post code. But hang on a minute, wasn't his hair a little grey? Turning to him I said, have you seen a ghost? My laughter echoed uneasily as he ignored me. Everyone was chatting, having a laugh about work or 'birds,' the usual lad banter and I realised he hadn't even acknowledged my presence. I glanced at him, worried that I'd somehow offended him and tried to cast my mind back to last week but could think of nothing. Really, nothing. The space in my head where last Friday should be was empty. Should I confront him? Ask him straight out what was wrong? No, I couldn't do that, all our mates were here and I'd look a right mug. I perked up as he turned, but he stared straight past me. I may as well not have been there.

I felt my anger growing, grabbed his shoulder and he noticed me at last. His mouth opened, his eyes widened, and he rubbed his arm as though I'd hurt it. The pint he was holding dropped to the floor as he stood up, backing away slowly before turning to run to the door. I could only sit, bewildered as he turned to give one last, terrified look.

I have to say, I'd no idea what to do and glanced at the lads to see what they'd made of it, but they were chatting away as though nothing had happened.

I decided to go after him, have it out properly and was hurrying through the room, elbowing my way through the throng, when a squeal of brakes and a horrendous bang stopped everyone in their tracks. A terrible, heart rendering scream echoed around the room and silence filled the pub. Then, everyone was running and shouting, and I was swept along with them, praying that Andy was alright.

Outside there was a scene of total mayhem. A young woman, shock and horror displayed all over her face, was being helped out of a bent, smoking car. A large group stood in a sketchy circle gazing at something on the ground, voices were calling for an ambulance and exclamations of dismay rang around the cobbles. A waitress from the pub was sitting on the kerb, head in hands, crying. I stood rooted, my heart beating so fast I thought it would burst, praying it wasn't Andy lying lifeless on the ground.

As the wailing ambulance arrived, a figure appeared, walking tentatively through the crowded lane. A vaguely human shape, surrounded by an undulating blue/grey vapour which slowly evaporated until I could see that it was Andy. As he approached, he smiled that broad friendly grin, here was the Andy that I'd always known.

"Hello, my old buddy," he said, as though nothing had happened, as though he'd never ignored me, as though he knew we'd be friends forever. I can't tell you how relieved I felt as he took my arm and led me back into the Golden Cross for a pint.

COVENTRY STARS OF STAGE AND SCREEN

By Margaret Egrot

A quick canter through some of the famous actors, directors and playwrights with Coventry connections.

Coventry hides its theatrical pedigree rather well. The city is known for ribbons and watches; the development of the motor industry; creating the first pedestrian shopping centre; winning the FA cup in 1987; and, since the English Civil War in the 1640s when the local Roundheads gave their Cavalier prisoners a shirty welcome, being the sort of place that people are sent to, rather than coming to of their own accord. Oh, and a story about a naked lady on a horse.

But take a second look. Hundreds of years ago Coventry was one of the centres in Britain for drama, it is home to the first civic theatre built after the Second World War and has the country's only professional Shop Front Theatre. It has also been the birthplace of some of our most noted players and playwrights, past and present (or has played a role in their journey to greater things). Many of the names below will be familiar to you, even if their link to Coventry is not.

According to the Bible: In the beginning God created the heaven and the earth (Genesis 1.1). Many millennia later Man created mystery plays to explain this and other Bible stories to ordinary people. (The word mystery comes from the Latin ministerium meaning craft or occupation, and the plays were written and performed by members of the different trade guilds). There were ten Coventry plays known to have existed at this time. They brought to life stories from the New Testament and were performed annually – starting near St Mary's Priory and then paraded round the town on wagons as pageants.

Only two of these pageants have survived into the twenty-first century. One is the Shearmen and Tailors' pageant, which includes the famous Coventry Carol that starts: Lullay, lullay /

Thou little tiny child / By-by lullay, sung allegedly by the women on hearing the decree for the massacre of the innocents. The other surviving pageant was performed by the guild of weavers.

The mystery plays were performed in Coventry from the end of the 14th century until they were banned in 1579, probably during the Protestant Reformation. These plays would have been seen as being too closely linked to the traditions of the Pope and the Catholic Church, and not therefore acceptable to the more zealous religious reformers in the reign of Elizabeth I.

They were not performed again for nearly four centuries. Then, in 1962, it was decided to use one to mark the consecration of the new cathedral in Coventry, which had been built after the old one had been almost completely destroyed during the blitz in November 1940.

Robert Prior-Pitt (1935 – 2020) was cast as Jesus. He was a newly married young Coventrian who had recently moved back to the city as a silk screen printer after failing to get enough acting work to pay for a mortgage in London. He became enthralled by the mystery plays and, in 1965, he was appointed as drama director at the new cathedral to revive the mystery play tradition. He also encouraged new drama, and exchanges with Coventry's twin cities in Germany (Kiel and Hamburg) and the American University of Valparaiso, as part of the cathedral's mission to promote peace and reconciliation. With subsequent support from the newly built Belgrade theatre, there were performances of the mystery plays throughout the 1970s, 1980s and 2000s.

In 1970 Robert Prior-Pitt took up the post of drama lecturer in Coventry Technical College and by 1984 he was head of the theatre department for the new Coventry Centre for Performing Arts. Many of his students get a mention later in this article.

William Shakespeare (1564 – 1616) was not born in Coventry, but his father was a prominent man in his home-town of Stratford – a mere twenty miles (or a full day's journey) down the road. It is believed that the young William used to accompany his father on business trips to Coventry so may well have seen some of the last mystery plays to be performed here.

Shakespeare senior (and son) may have also attended performances of new plays, as the city (the fourth largest in the country at the time) was one of the regular destinations for touring acting companies. Companies Shakespeare was known to have toured with as an unknown actor are recorded as being in the city during his early adulthood, so it is quite possible that he appeared on stage in the city too.

All new plays had to be performed first in front of the mayor, invited dignitaries, and members of their families – most probably in St Mary's Guildhall. The tapestry in the Guildhall is said to have influenced Shakespeare's interest in the history behind the plays he set during the Wars of the Roses. There are several mentions of Coventry in these plays: Falstaff and Bardolf are 'on the road to Coventry' in Henry IV part 1; battles take place in the city in Henry VI part III; and there is the meeting on what is now Gosford Green ordered by Richard 11 for the duel between the lords Bolingbroke and Mowbray. This in fact proved to be an anti-climax, from a theatrical point of view anyway, as the king decided to banish them instead. But banishment did allow Bolingbroke to stay alive and return to the country after a few years to claim what he and his supporters regarded as his rightful inheritance, overthrow Richard II, and become Henry IV – giving the plot for several more history plays that ended with Richard III.

The Welsh born actress Sarah Kemble (1755 – 1831) was married to William Siddons in Holy Trinity church in 1773 whilst on tour in the city. Sarah Siddons, as she was subsequently known, became famous for her depictions of Shakespeare characters, notably Lady Macbeth and Hamlet (actresses playing prominent male roles is not as new a phenomenon as we might think).

Less well known than Shakespeare and Sarah Siddons, but whose links to Coventry are a little better documented, is Ira Aldridge (1807 – 1867). He was the American-born son of slaves who was one of the few black children in New York to receive a decent early education that included trips to the theatre. Inspired by what he saw, he joined the African Grove Theatre at the age of 13. Slavery had not yet been abolished in America, it was not a safe place for an ambitious young black man, and his opportunities to perform on stage were severely limited. He and a friend set sail for England, where he felt his talents would be better received, and by the age of 17 he was playing Othello on the London stage (admittedly in a rather low-profile theatre). But his performances were noticed, and he was soon playing other major Shakespearean roles in bigger theatres in London, and elsewhere around the country. This included the Theatre Royal in Coventry. In 1828, at the tender age of 21, he became the actor-manager there, the first black actor-manager in the country.

As well as being passionate about acting, he was passionate about ending slavery. It had already been abolished in Britain, but he would address the local audiences after each performance about the situation elsewhere. As a result, he was instrumental in persuading Coventry to petition parliament to abolish slavery in the colonies. Ira Aldridge died at the age of 60 whilst touring in Poland. In 2017, on the 150th anniversary of his death, a blue plaque was unveiled at the site of the Theatre Royal. This had long since closed and been demolished, so the plaque was placed on the wall of the BHS shop, sadly now also closed.

A noted Shakespearean actor with a Coventry connection was Ellen Terry (1847 – 1928) who was born in the city. Both parents were actors in a touring company and she was destined for the stage from birth. She had no particular links to Coventry beyond infancy, appearing as she did in many theatres around the country including the Theatre Royal in Bristol, the Haymarket in

London, and with the Wigan theatre company where she first met Henry Irving.

Henry Irving subsequently rented the Lyceum Theatre, London, and invited Ellen Terry to join him. Acting opposite him, in mostly Shakespearean roles, she became the most famous actress on the world stage. When Irving's company ran out of money, she and her son took over the management of the Imperial Theatre, where they staged plays by new playwrights such as Bernard Shaw and Henrik Ibsen, and attracted a whole new audience to the theatre.

Ellen Terry's fame made her an obvious choice to open the new Empire theatre (formerly the Corn Exchange) in Hertford Street, Coventry, in 1906, her jubilee year. Again, this theatre is no more, but the foundation stone was saved and can now be found in the foyer of the Criterion Theatre, a small volunteer led theatre based in Earlsdon, Coventry.

T. E. Dunville (1867 – 1924) was born and brought up in Coventry. He is best known as a music hall comedian and was once described by Charlie Chaplin as 'an excellent funny man.' This did not inure him to depression however, and he committed suicide, aged 57.

Another actor with a link to the Criterion Theatre is Nigel Hawthorne (1929 – 2001). Like Ellen Terry, he was born in Coventry, but left at the age of three when his family moved to South Africa. He returned to England in the 1950s to pursue a career as an actor and is perhaps best known for his role as Sir Humphrey Appleby, the permanent secretary, in the sitcoms Yes Minister, and Yes Prime Minister. He also played an award-winning role as King George in Alan Bennett's stage play The Madness of George III, that was later made into a film in which he also starred. Although by this time a household name, he agreed to a request by the Criterion Theatre to become their patron and remained so until his death.

Derbyshire born Elizabeth Spriggs (1929 – 2008) moved as a child with her parents to a farm in Fillongley just outside Coventry. She taught speech and drama in Coventry before making her name with repertory theatres in Birmingham and Bristol, the Royal Shakespeare Company (RSC) and the National, as well as becoming a well-known face on the big and small screen.

Billie Whitelaw (1932 – 2014) was born in Coventry in the year that Nigel Hawthorne left the city. She too soon left and was brought up in Bradford where, despite the family being poor (her father died of lung cancer when she was nine), she started to make her name as a child actress and subsequently trained at RADA. Initially she specialised in playing blousy blondes, but in 1965 she memorably replaced Maggie Smith to play Desdemona opposite Laurence Olivier in Othello. Her chief claim to fame however is her professional partnership with the playwright, Samuel Beckett, who said that many of his more experimental plays – such as Happy Days – were created especially for her.

Sir Ian McKellen is still very much alive and is one of the country's foremost living actors, famous for his roles on both stage and screen. But it was in Coventry that he made his first professional appearance when he joined the Belgrade Theatre in 1961. The Belgrade was the first civic theatre to be built in Britain after the Second World War and opened officially in 1958, putting on progressive new dramas with a string of talented young actors and directors. Together with the new cathedral, the theatre symbolised an optimism for the future of the country generally, and Coventry in particular. The Belgrade, incidentally, is also the venue where, in 2017, it was officially announced that Coventry was to be the UK City of Culture in 2021.

Within four years of starting out at the Belgrade, Sir Ian was appearing in West End theatres, and he also performed on several occasions with the RSC in Stratford and London. In 2005 he fulfilled a lifelong ambition when he appeared in several episodes of Coronation Street. He is known as well, of course, for his career on the big screen, in particular, the box office hit Lord of the Rings.

In 2019, Sir Ian celebrated his eightieth birthday by touring Britain in his one-man autobiographical show. He returned to the regional theatres that had played a part in his life as an actor, including the Belgrade – where it had all started.

Other names associated with the pioneering days at the Belgrade include Arnold Wesker, Sir Trevor Nunn, Bob Carlton, Ron Hutchinson, Laurence Boswell, Clive Owen and Katy Stevens.

The playwright Arnold Wesker (1932 – 2016) was given his start at the Belgrade in 1958 with his new play Chicken Soup with Barley, which he had been unable to get staged anywhere else. He returned in 1959 with Roots, which starred Joan Plowright and later transferred to the West End. Always a dogged individualist, he returned to Coventry in the early 1970s when the RSC refused to put on his latest play The Journalists, (which they deemed was too controversial). He agreed to the Criterion's offer to step in and reported that he was pleased with their interpretation when he came to watch it.

Ipswich born Sir Trevor Nunn won a scholarship to become a trainee director at the Belgrade before forging an impressive career at the RSC (he directed Sir Ian McKellen in Macbeth there in 1976, to critical acclaim), The National, and elsewhere. In 2008 he returned to the Belgrade to direct Scenes from a Marriage starring his third wife, Imogen Stubbs.

Bob Carlton (1950 – 2018) was born and educated in Coventry. His association with the Belgrade also stems from the time he won a scholarship with them as a trainee director. He is perhaps best known now for his juke box musical Return to the Forbidden Planet (1989)

Ron Hutchinson is known as an Irish screen writer and playwright and the author of, among other things, Moonlight and Magnolias. What is not so well known is that his family moved to Coventry when he was young and he also cut his teeth at the Belgrade. Much of his work reflects the experiences of Irish people living and working away from home which would resonate with many of the Irish who had moved to Coventry. He did not however write specifically about Coventry. One Irish playwright who did, was Tom Murphy (1935 – 2018). He is not recorded as having set foot in Coventry but used the city as the backdrop for his play – A Whistle in the Dark – about the tensions and social challenges experienced by Irish immigrants to Britain.

Laurence Boswell, who has directed big names like Madonna and Eddie Izzard, is Coventry born and educated. He has talked about 'the extraordinary support' he received as a young actor and director at the Belgrade Youth Theatre. He returned to The Belgrade in 2014 for his Spanish Golden Age Season.

Clive Owen was born and educated in Coventry and is now famous on both sides of the Atlantic for performances on stage, in film, and television. He also started out at the Belgrade in the late 1980s, where he worked with the budding young director, Laurence Boswell. He subsequently became better known in the UK for his role in the ITV series, Chancer (1990) before moving to America. His first major Hollywood role was in The Rich Man's Wife alongside Halle Berry. He has retained his stage career, starring in a highly acclaimed theatre revival of Peter Nichols' play A Day in the Death of Joe Egg and, more recently, in the West End production of Tennessee Williams' The Night of the Iguanas.

Katy Stevens is another award-winning British actor who has lived and worked in Coventry and performed extensively at the Belgrade in both classical dramas and pantomime.

Several other actors, such as Terence Davies, who are not normally associated with Coventry started their training here, often under direction of Robert Prior-Pitt. Davies is now one of Britain's most acclaimed filmmakers. Whilst he was a student in Coventry, he wrote the screenplay for Children (1976), and then went on to write Madonna and Child, and Death and Transfiguration. The three films, largely autobiographical, were screened together at film festivals across Europe and America, as The Terence Davies Trilogy, and have won many awards.

Much of his other work is also autobiographical, and he has adapted the work of other writers, including Virginia Woolf, Emily Dickenson, Edith Wharton, and Terence Rattigan. Productions of his work have been relatively limited by his desire to work on what interests him rather than what makes money at the box office.

Jeffrey Kissoon came to Coventry College of Education where he trained as a drama teacher. His first teaching post was at St Peter and St Paul's primary school in the city. Born in Trinidad, he arrived in Britain at the age of ten, had his first acting experience whilst in school in London and, following his stint as a teacher in Coventry, became a full-time actor in the early 1970s.

Jeffrey continued to tutor aspiring actors and directors whilst his own acting career expanded. It includes working with the RSC, and many other companies around the country. He has also appeared on television (Grange Hill and EastEnders) and with Lenny Henry in the BBC Radio 4 sitcom Rudy's Rare Records (later turned into a play and performed at the Birmingham Rep). He directs plays and is, among other roles, on the Board of directors for the Warehouse Theatre, Croydon, London.

Ron Cook moved to Coventry when he was six and was educated at Wyken Croft junior school and Caludon Castle. He must be one of very few schoolboys who was advised by his headmaster to try acting as a career rather than going for a 'proper' job. He took the advice and went to the Rose Burford College to study drama. One of his teachers at secondary school was Geoff Bennett, a founder member of the Criterion Theatre, and Ron made a number of appearances there before becoming a professional actor.

Ron Cook has appeared in numerous theatres around the country and in a large number of television productions including Bergerac, Black Adder, Dr Who, several instalments of the BBC's The Complete Works of William Shakespeare and, in 2019, in Netflix's The Witcher. He has also appeared on the big screen, including playing the role of Napoleon Bonaparte in both Sharpe (1994) and Quills (2000). He is currently a patron of the Criterion Theatre and his letter of acceptance is displayed in the foyer.

Playwright Chris O'Connell and producer Julia Negus are both names inextricably linked with the current Coventry theatre scene. Both are alumni of Coventry University – Chris completed an MA in theatre there, and Julia studied visual arts. In 1992 they founded Theatre Absolute and plays written by Chris for the theatre include the Edinburgh Fringe award winning Street Trilogy (Car, Raw, Kid). He also performed and directed at the Criterion throughout the 1980s.

In 2009, tired of touring and aligning their work to available funding streams, they approached Coventry City Council to see if they could use one of the empty premises in the city as a 'pop-up' theatre. The council offered them the empty fish and chip shop at the bottom of the City Arcade. Within months they had opened the UK's only professional Shop Front Theatre. The theatre is still going strong, specialising in original and experimental work, and supporting emerging writers whose work they feel is new and relevant to the city and beyond.

Some actors who spent at least part of their early life in Coventry and made, or are now making, their names elsewhere, include Carmen Silvera (1922 – 2002), Hazel O'Connor, Jefferson Hall, and Jennie Jacques.

Carmen Silvera (1922 – 2002) was born in Canada to a Jamaican father who had Coventry connections. They moved to the city when she was a child. She is best known for her role in the TV series 'Allo, 'Allo. The year before she died, she returned to Coventry for the production at the Belgrade of You're Only Young Twice – and took the opportunity for a sentimental reunion with old school friends.

Hazel O'Connor is unlikely to return to the city for any reunions. Though born in the city she had an unhappy home life and ran away when she was sixteen. She lived a nomadic existence for the next few years before her acting and singing talents were noticed, in particular in the 1980 production of Breaking Glass for which she wrote the songs and also played the role of Kate.

Jefferson Hall, who used the name Robert Hall in his early career, was born in Coventry and is perhaps best known now for his role as Hugh of the Vale in Game of Thrones.

Jennie Jacques was also born in Coventry. Her first major role was as Annie Miller in the 2009 BBC series Desperate Romantics about the Pre-Raphaelite Brotherhood. More recently she has played the part of the Saxon Queen, Judith, in Vikings.

Debbie Issit, on the other hand, was born and brought up in Birmingham, but her name has been strongly linked to Coventry since her film Nativity! premiered in the Skydome Arena. The film is about a failed actor, turned schoolteacher in Coventry, who reluctantly takes on the task of producing the school's nativity play. The film is set in and around the cathedral and proved to be the most successful independent film for 2009 in Britain. In 2012 she did a follow up: Nativity 2 – Danger in the Manger, which made twice as much at the box office as the first film and, more recently, Nativity 3 – Dude Where's My Donkey? However, these films were not the first time Debbie Issit had been to Coventry – as with a number of other successful actors, writers and directors, she has credited the drama classes she attended in the city – and Robert Prior-Pitt – with starting her on the path to success.

Robert Prior-Pitt was a link between Coventry's medieval past and, through his own performances and teaching, the city's more recent place in the history of stage and screen. Another Coventry resident has also, albeit accidentally, reached across an even greater span. Remember the naked lady on a horse mentioned in the opening paragraph?

Lady Godiva, the wife of the eleventh century Lord Leofric, was reputed to have ridden naked through the streets of Coventry in a bid to dissuade her husband from increasing his taxation of the townspeople. Whether she actually took all her clothes off, rode bare-back, simply removed her jewellery, or stayed happily at home, remains a matter of debate. But her ride is an integral part of Coventry's history and it will no doubt feature in the 2021 celebrations.

In 1982, in a bid to cheer people up during a recession (the city had yet to win the FA cup) a local beauty queen, Pru Poretta, was asked to play the part of Lady Godiva in a one-off revival of the city's carnival procession. Nearly forty years later she is still playing the role and can be said to have made the part uniquely her own.

Usually clad in a rich red velvet gown – and never performing naked to my knowledge – she has paraded through the city on horseback, steamroller, and tractor; even travelling by helicopter on one occasion. As Lady Godiva, she has opened events, shops and retirement homes, and has gone into schools to teach children about the Godiva tradition. Along the way, she has also raised thousands of pounds for local charities.

Pru Poretta never thought, in 1982, that her role as Lady Godiva would still be so popular in Coventry. But perhaps we shouldn't be surprised. So much of the city's history – the Godiva legend; the early mystery plays; the old and new cathedral; the interest in innovation and experimentation (not just in motor cars and other machines, but in theatre and other arts); and the historic anti-authoritarian tendency, are ingrained in the city's DNA.

Ingrained too in the city's rich culture to be celebrated in various forms throughout 2021.

DOUBLE TAKE AT 'AN ARUNDEL TOMB'

By John Greatrex

Philip Larkin was Coventry's most famous poet. He attended
Henry VIII School and in later life became the Head Librarian at
Hull University. His plaque in Poets' Corner, Westminster
Abbey, quotes the last line of his poem An Arundel Tomb....
"What will survive of us is love".

Have you been to Chichester? Have you seen the tomb?
Stand in the cathedral one quiet afternoon and read
What Mr. Larkin wrote about the countess and her squire.
Now look at the tomb, now again at the words and decide

If the poet's a liar. Observe the actual tomb – this
Symbol of eternal love. Which hand is it, the left or
Right, without the glove? He states the left. But is
It true? From what I saw when I was there, unless I'm

Much mistaken, it's the other one that's bare. Well,
It's not what I expected and it's quite a tender shock
Discovering a mirage where you thought you'd see a rock
But does it really matter? Who's to say a writer's

Bound by truth? Perhaps he simply saw the tomb the
Wrong way round. When there note too the sword has
Snapped. No doubt, some Tudor afternoon, a boy, his
Tutor's back was turned, leaned heavily upon the tomb.

Also, a nose has been replaced with a slightly different
Coloured stone. Who knows? Maybe these alterations
Were the sculpture's own. Jealous that Time would break
His work, he chose himself to be the rack.

Like Prospero. Destroyed his book: Excalibur thrown back. "Ah, what is Truth?" as Pilate asked. Things remembered? Things Forgot? Is everything we take as fact mere speculation? Based on what?

INSPIRED TO WRITE 21 WORDS FROM OUR COVER ILLUSTRATION

Coventry Writers' Group's Secretary, Hilary Hopker, painted the beautiful picture of Bayley Lane for the anthology cover. It inspired some of the group to write 21 words to mark Coventry, UK City of Culture 2021.

Ode 21 to Coventry
Lady Godiva, Peeping Tom
Bless the city I am from
COVID vaccine bottle shake
And first in the world to inoculate!
Bev Woodley
*

Memories flow down Bayley Lane from plague to Covid.
Let's beat the odds, make more, to celebrate
the CITY of CULTURE.
Judith E Roberts
*

A Cov Street Symphony
Bells ring, cans clank past
ska front in Tudor timber,
cobbles swing down streets.
Breeze sings to leaves
beneath sky-blue ceiling.
Emilie Lauren Jones
*

Once glorious, then humbled;
Basil Spence's gothic genius,
 a ruined hollow.
Still you stand, majestic and eternal,
 our symbol of reconciliation.
Nuzo Onoh
*

After Coventry's last hanging,
Mary's body was buried upright under the cobbled street.
A restless eternity hearing nothing but tourist's feet.
Hilary Hopker
*

Our City 2020
Coventry Expands
As the Covid world shrinks.
Rivers! Canal! Cemetery! Pound! Castle wall!
Parks! Woodland walks!
Hello!!
Daily small /
Immense pleasures.
Margaret Egrot
*

Gallows Day
Come, imbibe with me at the Golden Cross.
There's a hanging on Friday, plenty to see.
Bring the children with thee.
Margaret Mather
*

Culture in the city
Inside a crumbling pizzeria
The maitre d'hotel's penny-farthing
Stood us guard
While we gorged on tiramisu
To the strains of Debussy
Taffi Nywanza
*

Bayley Lane
Bayley lane, that historic cobbled street I walked down as
hope-filled teenager and adult, ultimately marrying in St
Mary's secret undercroft.
Alex Bartlett
*

Cobbled stones,
sandstone walls.
A thousand years have now flown.
Survived through history,
disasters and victory.
Could the stonemasons have known.
Ann Evans
*

Time has not taken from you,
But only added to your mystery,
Of an age that remains
Forever in our history.
Mary Ogilvie
*

Invented;
bicycles,
jet engines,
black cabs,
roads shaped like rings.
A brief annotation;
a sad association –
Women putting cats into bins.
David Court
*

How Times Change
Bells ring,
glistening,
like newly-minted degrees.
Sweaty, nervous fingers grasp excitedly,
sharing the future.
Promise-filled rings shine.
Reflecting changes in time.
Ella Cook
*

GUILDHALL VISITOR

By Hilary Hopker

The caretaker couldn't understand what was wrong. He'd oiled the hinges but there was still a horrible high-pitched noise every time he opened the counting room door. In the end he told David to miss that room off the tour.

Lottie had enjoyed greeting Guildhall visitors – until last night. The Americans used to make her smile with their camera phones and exclamations that the hall was definitely part of the Harry Potter set. The medieval hall with its warm sandstone walls, high stained-glass windows and tapestry at one end was certainly a dramatic setting, but it was all authentic.

As real as the pain Lottie was in today. Even the school trip couldn't cheer her up. Normally she liked to peek in the kid's lunchboxes or ruffle the papers on their clipboard, but today she just wanted them gone.

Her happiest moments had always been the ones when she had the hall to herself. Often, she would sing, the hall had excellent acoustics. Nursery rhymes, songs from school, the odd tune off the radio. It's amazing the things you never forget. Once she'd even tried on a suit of armour before getting scared she would get stuck inside it.

Normally though she would pick up her skirts and dance across the parquet hall floor, imagining Richard was leading her in the waltz.

When the tourists were in, she sometimes made mischief. Nothing big, rattling the odd teacup or blowing gently on the back of people's necks as they went down the spiral staircase. She always tried hard not to giggle and give herself away when they looked round confused.

Then after years, last night she had seen him. Richard. It was another one of those dinner things and she was planning to drop a guidebook off the balcony when she heard a familiar step. She suddenly wanted to touch him again, look deeply into his eyes and see if he missed her as much as she missed him.

Then she had seen Julie, her old next-door neighbour, holding onto his arm laughing. For a moment the hall had gone blurry, just lights and shadows. That beautiful tapestry became nothing more than a smudge of reds and browns.

She had raced down the spiral stairs, bumping off walls, running towards them. Of course, they never saw her coming. Lottie grabbed Julie's wine glass and smashed it to the floor, before storming off to the kitchen.

The cooks ran out screaming. Most of the tomato tins bounced off the wall but some had broken on impact, leaving a satisfying red explosion.

Now Lottie felt ashamed as she endlessly traced the words 'til death us do part' across the cold marble floor with her finger.

David ignored the sign. As he opened the door a high-pitched sound came from the empty counting room, uncannily like a woman wailing. He closed the door and ushered the children away.

*

St Mary's Guildhall in Coventry was built in 1342 and is the finest surviving medieval guildhall in the country. The Guildhall acted as the focus of guild business, chiefly as a ceremonial space, meeting place, and banqueting hall.

The hall is rumoured to have several ghosts, including, a monk, a grey lady and a little girl. St Mary's has a room known as the *drapers' room* which is rumoured to be very emotional, with many people being overcome with a feeling of sadness and some even bursting into tears for no reason.

DAISY'S HOEDOWN

By Margaret Mather

My relationship with my mother, Daisy, had always been a little bit hit and miss. Sometimes we were inseparable, at other times; we couldn't wait to see the back of each other. I loved my mum but we were two very different people so when she asked if she could move in with me after dad died, I was unsure but felt trapped into letting her stay.

Bill, my husband had thought it a bad idea but with our children grown up and living their own lives, it seemed churlish to refuse although for the life of me I didn't know why she'd want to move from her beautiful home in Gibbet Hill, Coventry to my modest semi in the Tile Hill area of the city. She'd said the house was too big for her and she'd felt lonely on her own.

Mum settled in well and three months after dad's passing was ready to resume her social life. I still grieved for my father. As the days and weeks rolled on, it began to annoy me the way she seemed to shrug off his passing. She rarely spoke about him, and I never saw her cry once.

"No time to waste crying, Jessie. Carpe Diem, seize the day. Life is for living, and that's exactly what I'm doing."

I was shocked at Mum's attitude and overnight a frosty atmosphere developed between us. She did her own thing, and I simmered. Our roles reversed. I was the one who constantly worried about her when she went out at night.

"Don't be late and don't make a noise when you come back. Some of us have work in the morning," I'd shout as mother headed for the door, her long grey coat opening just a little to reveal something blue and sparkly underneath and carrying a shoulder bag that bulged with goodness knows what. I was intrigued but would not give her the satisfaction of asking where she was going.

Parcels arrived for her almost daily; the empty cardboard boxes by the bin were a testament to that. Mum never said what had been in them and I never asked. At seventy-two she was vulnerable, and I feared for her wellbeing. She needed protection and I decided it was up to me to find out where she was going.

The following evening, I said goodbye as she left the house and waited a few minutes before hastily pulling on my warm, navy blue coat. Keeping my distance, I followed behind. At the end of the street, she stopped and looked around. I quickly dashed into a neighbour's drive out of sight, feeling like Inspector Clouseau in a Pink Panther movie. When I looked again, she was climbing into an Uber. I was flabbergasted. She had arranged an Uber yet I didn't know how to download the app, let alone call one. The next time she ventured out, I would follow by car. I didn't have long to wait.

Two nights later she was off again. I trailed at a discrete distance concentrating on the taxi as it sped through the streets and only vaguely aware of my surroundings. It wasn't until we stopped at the Lime Tree Park Working Men's club in Templar Avenue that I dared to breathe.

I wondered why we were there. It wasn't a place my mother frequented then I watched dumbfounded as she got out of the car and walked into the club. I couldn't believe my eyes. She would never have gone into a place like that on her own if dad had been alive. This was serious I had to find out what she was up to.

Hurrying in after her, I was immediately stopped by a man wearing a threadbare tweed jacket and a flat cap, sitting at a kiosk by the entrance. "Are you a member?" he asked, showing teeth, stained brown by years of smoking.

"No," I replied. "I want to talk to my mother; she's just walked in, blonde haired lady, long grey coat she..."

"Sorry, luv, but you'll have to pay to get in."

"What? I only want to speak to her. I'm not staying."

"Rules are rules, me duck, that'll be two pounds please," he said, thrusting a grubby hand towards me.

I practically threw the coins at him. "Jobs worth," I muttered under my breath as I headed for the bar.

There was no sign of mum in the bar or the lounge, the only room left was the concert room maybe she was playing bingo.

Slowly I opened the door a fraction and peeped round only to be greeted by my mother, line dancing to the strains of *Achy Breaky Heart*.

I stood there frozen to the spot.

My mother, dressed like Calamity Jane, sporting a yellow and white check shirt with black fringes dangling down from the sleeves, blue denim jeans with sequins dotted all over and pink glittery cowboy boots. I cringed at the very sight of her making a show of herself. Now I understood what the parcels had contained.

Moving as one the dancers with their bright coloured clothes swirled and sparkled as they turned, kicked and flicked their way through a flurry of dances slapping their thighs and clapping in symmetry while laughing and giggling. Mum was in the middle of it all, having the time of her life.

While gazing at the spectacle unfolding before my eyes, realisation dawned. Mum was actually enjoying herself for the first time in years.

Looking after dad, year in year out as his health deteriorated had not been easy for her. He'd been a difficult patient and she'd spent all her time caring for him. Now she was enjoying life to the full.

Suddenly shame engulfed me. She was only making the best of the years she had left. I should be helping her do that, not making things harder.

Time I got to grips with reality and stopped acting like a child. Mum deserved to be happy.

Quietly, I closed the door and left her to enjoy the hoedown.

CON-FUSION

By Maxine Burns

Apple samosas, hot curried peas
Coriander and cumin waft on the breeze.
Ramadan, Diwali, Christmas and Ede
Dreadlocks with ribbons and colourful beads

Jasmine tea, Saki, curry and chips,
Hot crisp pitta with yoghurty dips.
Foods without borders
Spicy and gorgeous,
beneath Coventry's steeples
Fusion food, fusion people.

SKY BLUE

By Nuzo Onoh

The pigeon is perched on the roof of my brand-new BMW, fluffing its feathers and staring around with a pair of little, hard eyes that glitter with maniacal glee. With its grey-black feathers and rotundity, it's no different from the other greedy pigeons in our Hillfields neighbourhood, save for the black rings around its eyes. At first glance, I think the pigeon is blind, a victim of cruel pranksters who've plucked out its eyes, leaving behind two black and empty sockets devoid of sight and awareness.

Pigeons are a nuisance in our low-income street and are loathed with equal vitriol across the residents that make up our diverse populace. Their white shit-blitz is the blight of cars, laundry, pavements, garden slabs, pushchair-trapped babies and exposed clean hair. I wouldn't be surprised therefore, if some frustrated victim has decided to inflict dire revenge on one of the little shite-machines by goring out its eyes or punching it black and blue.

Except the plump bugger perched atop Sky Blue, my expensive, brand new BMW 4 Series Sports Convertible, blue metallic colour, isn't blind; not by a long shot. Even as I glare at it with growing annoyance, the wretched bird twitches its bum and splashes my girl with watery, white mess. If Sky Blue could talk, I'm sure she'll be screaming louder than me. As it is, all she can do is sit there in her majestic beauty and take the gross insult of the stinky pigeon with silent resignation.

Not I, though; hell no! I shout at the pigeon and almost fling my key-bunch at it, such is my rage. But I stop myself in the nick of time, fearful of denting my day-old car. I worked hard to save up the deposit for my girl and I'm now mortgaged to her for the next three years. No way am I going to allow the tiniest scratch to mar Sky Blue's beauty till I win over the admiration and affection of another cool lady, Shaniqua Wright, the Rhianna cum Beyoncé of our workplace at the energy contact centre. Take it from me, it's pretty rare to come across a twenty-something, fit black guy like me cruising around Coventry in a mega-oppressor car like my BMW 4 Series Sports Convertible, and something just tells me that Shaniqua will be mine once she samples a ride inside the plush leather-clad interior of my gleaming new car.

So, despite my annoyance with the shite-arse pigeon, I hold tight to my car key and instead, wave my arms wildly as I dash towards Sky Blue, wishing I could strangle that vile bird dead on the spot. I know I've no hope in hell of catching the bugger, but I'll be damned if I just stand by and let it disrespect my new car.

The pigeon does the unexpected. Rather than flying off in the usual ungraceful flight of its kind, it simply hops away from its wet shite and lands on the bonnet of my car, staring at me with the same hard, glassy malice.

"Freaking shitbag!" I sprint towards the front of my car in my shiny blue loafers that's a perfect match to Sky Blue, hoping to scare it away before it messes up my bonnet with its vile paint. "Eff off, you stinky bugger; shoo… off with you, you fat bastard." I'm still waving my arms furiously, diving low to squash the fat sod dead. But I'm not fast enough. The dirty sod does the familiar arse-twitch and drops another white bomb on Sky Blue's bonnet before finally flying off to our neighbour's roof, staring down at me as I rage and stump.

I dash back into the semi-detached I share with my mum and grab a kitchen towel before rushing outside again. With manic vigour, I wipe off the vile mess, cursing everything with wings and feathers to eternal damnation. One of these days… just you wait and see; one of these days I'll be stinking rich, make enough dough to get Mum and me away for good from this shitty, pigeon-deluged neighbourhood. My mood is as dark as my navy leather jacket and when I finally get into my car to make my way to my workplace, I'm still cursing the pigeon under my breath.

As I drive out from my mum's driveway, I take another quick glance at our neighbour's rooftop. Sure enough, the black-eyed sod is still there, its glassy, beady eyes glittering with what I take for malice and glee. Freaking Bastard! I hope you get eaten by an eagle! I give it the middle finger and turn on the music at top blast, feeling both the car and my body vibrate joyfully from the heavy drumbeats. I'm starting to feel good once again, and my heart thrills as I run my hands gently over the smooth steering and the polished dashboard of my new baby. Even the leather seats smell expensive, more exclusive than the Paco Rabane men's cologne I recently bought for myself to go with my new polished image.

I reach over to the dashboard to activate the in-car (convertible) roof button. Instantly, the fresh summer breeze hits my skin, cooling my temper as the car roof slides smoothly into the rear of the BMW. I inhale and exhale deeply. I'm at peace with the whole world and its brothers, cousins and lovers. It's hard to resist the urge to wave at everyone stood at the traffic lights by Pool Meadow Bus Station and call out, "Hey, dude! Take a look at my cool car!" Instead, I ramp up the volume of my Drake CD, *'Find your Love'*, hoping its deafening beats would attract the attention I desperately crave. It's still a shock to me that I'm driving this cool princess of a car, and my heart is fit to burst with pride when several heads turn towards Sky Blue and I.

Down at the office, I manoeuvre into a tight spot in the parking lot and saunter out of my car, waiting till a couple of guys come closer before I raise back the car-roof remotely with my key. I hope the guys take notice and realise the cool ride belongs to none other than me... me, Ade Oluyele Williams, this fit Nigerian-British hunk that might just one day become the next Jay-Z of the British music industry. Yaah Babes!

They do. Their eyes take a second look at Sky Blue's gleaming beauty and their smiles are suddenly very friendly, their "Hey mate!" even friendlier as we all walk into the office for another long day of customer service drudgery. I'm just buying time here you understand, biding my time till I hit paydirt as a music production mogul. Still, I manage to catch a glimpse of Shaniqua at breaktime and casually drop a few words about my new BMW 4 Series Sports Convertible, blue metallic colour, automatic, on-board computer and all. I think I see a spark of interest in her light brown eyes and quickly offer her a ride home anytime she needs one, even today, I'm quick to add.

Shaniqua thanks me and says she drives. But who knows? she smiles coolly. Maybe her car might just misbehave one of these days and she'll take me up on my offer. I watch as she sashays back to her desk, knowing hundreds of other male eyes follow the progress of her killer backside with the same admiration and desire that burns in my heart. My mood plunges but I refuse to be deterred. One way or another, I'll find a way to lure her into my cool Sky Blue. I return to my desk and hook on my headphone, ready for the next call. The day drags till I'm ready to hang up the phone on the next customer that asks about their bloody tariffs and blasted bills. But eventually, it comes to an end around six o'clock and I'm more than ready to exit the building for good. It's a Friday evening and The Empire Coventry Club has a live band waiting to rock my weekend.

I pick up my mobile and key-bunch and troop out of the large building with the rest of the tired employees rushing towards the car park with the robotic sameness of our daily grind. I see my Sky Blue shimmering under the summer sun, her pale blue colour the same as the bright skies above. I'm stunned anew by her dazzling beauty. Then, in a blink, I'm stunned by a pain that sends me flying right across several parking bays till I land on hard concrete. I'm not sure I have time to figure out what's just happened before darkness overwhelms me and I give in gratefully to painless oblivion.

*

I wake up in a hospital bed and find my mother beside me, together with some blond-haired, white guy whose face is familiar though I can't put a name to the face. His smile is both strained and relieved and he's almost obsequious in his concern for my well-being. Mum glares at him with hatred as he speaks, apologising for my injuries, explaining how he just couldn't figure out what happened, how his foot somehow slipped and stayed on the pedal till I was hit. He's promising to do everything to help... anything mate. Mate? I'd laugh if the pain weren't stealing my sanity. Now, I know why his face is familiar. He's the arrogant prat whose uncle owns our private energy firm. Never liked him and his haughty ways and this is the first time he's deigned to speak to me in over two years of faithful service to his uncle's company.

Mum mumbles something under her breath in her native Yoruba language, something uncomplimentary. The vicious look in her eyes leaves no doubt about her feelings. The blond-haired guy blushes and fiddles with his red silk tie. He understands Mum's feelings even if he can't make out a word of her Nigerian lingo. I try to reach out for Mum's hand and squeeze her into polite silence, but my arms are both in heavy cast, including my right leg. I feel the bandage around my head and thank my luck that whatever injuries I've sustained to my head haven't turned me into a zombie. I can still remember my new BMW and I start to panic about Sky Blue getting vandalised in the office parking lot. I want to tell the nervous nephew fidgeting at the foot of my hospital bed, that he can go put a round-the-clock security on my car which lies abandoned at his uncle's office. But, I'm incapable of speech, thanks to the unfamiliar gap in my front teeth, the tight bandage, and the mind-numbing pain that fogs my mind.

In a wink, I fall into a deep sleep again and a few days later, I regain both my awareness and my greed and sign the contract forms presented to me by the ambulance-chaser from Messrs Bainbridge-Brown & Co, whom Mum brings to my bedside. The legal guy tells me my claim is worth just over fifty thousand pounds, especially as I've permanently lost two front teeth together with my other injuries. I think both Mum and I gasp at the same time. No freaking way! I'm thinking Sky Blue will finally be all mine, free from all loan obligations once I get my hand on the money. In fact, I'm feeling pretty thankful to that pompous prat of a nephew for knocking off my black arse with his car and bringing me this mammoth windfall. Freaking hell! Am I lucky or what?

But the best is still to come. Shaniqua turns up at the hospital to visit me a couple of days later. My heart almost stops when I see her swagger into the ward with attitude, her tight skirt hugging her sexy hips while her high heels make little clacks on the hard flooring of my ward. She smiles into my eyes, her long fake lashes highlighting the smouldering look in her dark eyes, and before she leaves, she leans low to kiss my cheek. Yaah Babes! Bring it on, Sister! I think I'm ready to meet my maker! Shaniqua's perfume lingers in my nostrils long after she's gone, together with the soft feel of her lips. I float into drowsy paradise, imagining the feel of those lips on mine once I fix my broken teeth.

Several sessions later with the physiotherapist, dentist and out-patient doctors and I'm totally healed. I receive my compensation pay-out and become the proud debt-free owner of my blue princess. Mum gets several thousand pounds from my largess which thrills her no end. She says she'll save it towards my deposit when I'm ready to buy my own digs and nothing I say will make her spend the money on herself. Our neighbour, another African lady from Ghana, says it's the single-parent mentality screwing up Mum's priorities, that habitual guilt trip of self-sacrifice and deprivation built into the DNA of most lone-parents. I'm thinking I'll have to ask Shaniqua to take her shopping one of these days, since Mum has so far refused to set foot in my car. She loathes Sky Blue with a passion and calls her the devil's ride. Sometimes, it's as if Mum's afraid of Sky Blue and always averts her eyes whenever she's near the poor car. She has no rational explanation for her aversion and simply says there's something wrong with the car, something very bad. Ha! You're so right, Mum. Sky Blue is one cool, badass chick and I wouldn't have her any other way! Anyway, I know it's Mum's usual superstitious mind at work and I've told her I have no intentions of hopping onto bus 17 at St Benedict's School bus-stop with her – hell no! I'm hoping Shaniq will make her see sense, though.

Yeah, forgot to mention that we're now an item, Shaniqua and I. Ever since the accident, we've grown closer, especially after the CEO uncle made me a team-leader in his firm to compensate for his nephew's damage to my body. The pay is almost double my old salary and these days, the money's just flowing in sweet and steady, and Shaniq and I are even starting to talk forever-togetherness.

Mum isn't too thrilled, as she'd prefer I go steady with an African girl, preferably a Yoruba girl from her Pentecostal church. She says Caribbean people have spent too long with white people that they now behave like the whites and expect a man to prepare his own meal, wash dishes, and even change a baby's diapers. Her grumbles slip into my right ear and quickly fly out of my left ear. I tell her she might as well resign herself to having a Jamaican daughter-in-law and happily blind my eyes to her martyred face.

*

The pigeon is perched atop Sky Blue's roof when I walk into our snow-covered street one freezing winter morning. I stare at it with goggled eyes, my mouth stretched so wide a whole melon could fit into it. No freaking way! I recognise the punched-up black eyes and their familiar glassy malice. It's the same shite-machine that sprayed my car on that terrible day of my accident just over a year ago. How could I forget the sod? Even as I stare in disbelief, it twitches its fat backside and splats its disgusting, white mess once again on my roof.

"Freaking dirty bastard!" I scream as I run towards Sky Blue. I slip on the snow and fall to the ground, sending a coat of icy white flakes flying into the air before settling on my expensive winter coat and fashion-bald head, bringing involuntary shivers to my body. By the time I scramble to my knees, the pigeon is on Sky Blue's bonnet, waiting patiently for me, hanging in there till I'm just within a few steps of its blasted neck before it does its familiar rude stuff with its arse and plonks its mess on the bonnet, exactly as the last time a year ago.

A feeling of déjà vu pricks my mind as I find myself repeating the same old crazed actions, cursing it as it flies atop our neighbour's roof, wiping off the mess with a kitchen towel before getting behind the wheel for another long day at the office. Again, I take a final glance at the neighbour's roof as I drive off and just as I expect, the pigeon is staring at me with that uncanny intelligence that sends an inexplicable feeling of unease down my spine.

With a violent shake of my head, I shake off the bad feeling and turn on the heating and my Kanye CD. Soon, the hypnotic beat of *'Stronger'* gradually revs up my energy for the tough day ahead. Being a team-leader hasn't made my work any easier, you know. I still have to deal with complaints from aggrieved customers and disgruntled workers as well as keep up with training and bloody KPIs.

Only bright spot at the office is my beautiful Shaniq, whose companionship I get to share through the day and the few nights at our fav B&B, enjoying long weekends of hot shenanigans and endless bottles of Prosecco. Like me, Shaniq still lives with her parents, who are God-fearing folks like my mum. That's one thing we Africans share in common with our Caribbean siblings—a strong love for Jesus and His churches, Baptist, Methodist, Mormons, Catholic, Anglican, Jehovah's Witnesses, Pentecostal, Joel Osteen, Creflo Dollar or one Pastor Enoch Adeboye. Preach it, brother! Preach it! Can't recall the last time a brother preached JC or His apostles to me, and Mum has finally given up trying to emotionally blackmail me into the sanctified hall of Holy Ghost Zone church in Hillfields.

Down at the office, I'm about to take my lunch break when my mobile phone rings. Mum's been in an accident and has been rushed to The University Hospital at Walsgrave, the police lady at the other end says, her clipped voice an unnatural blend of sympathy and professionalism. My heart is pounding as I rush towards the parking lot and into Sky Blue's serene interior. I'm praying, praying hard to a God I've never really given much attention to, begging Him to spare Mum's life, to keep her safe for me, let her live to see her grandkids that I'll have with Shaniq and the lovely house I'll buy for her in Nigeria. I know it's Mum's dream to return to Nigeria when she retires, and my dream is to make her dream a reality. I'm her only child and she's sacrificed everything for me. I know I have a father who's somewhere in Lagos with his other family. Never seen him except when I was a baby, which doesn't count. Mum's all I have and I'm all she has.

By the time I arrive at the hospital, Mum's dead. They say it's a freak accident, a falling piece of masonry from construction work in one of the council buildings in the city centre. She'd been out shopping, just shopping. When I collect her shopping bags, the familiar paper bags with the Primark label, I see a new shirt and pyjamas for me amongst her other stuff. Till the last day of her life, Mum thought of me and my wellbeing, as ever. My tears are hard, painful and long. My chest is gripped by a tight band that threatens to steal my breath. I'm unable to drive Sky Blue out of the hospital parking lot with my shaking limbs and pounding head. Instead, I take a taxi home, leaving Mum's cold and crushed body behind on the A&E bed.

I return to our house, our eerily quiet house without the familiar sound of Judge Judy dispensing justice with her usual acerbic wit, Mum's favourite TV programme. By the time the Yoruba community and the members of her Pentecostal church congregation start to arrive for condolence visits, I'm almost in a state of catatonia. But for Shaniq's loving support during the terrible weeks that follow Mum's death and funeral, by now, I'll be looking for a bridge to jump.

Just as happened with my accident, I use the services of Messrs Bainbridge-Brown & Co again and by the time Mum's estate is wound up, I inherit not just her large pension lump-sum pay-out and Life Insurance, but also, the massive compensation for her wrongful death claim. I suddenly find myself a millionaire... yes, a millionaire with more money than I know what to do with.

I'm still living in Mum's two-bedroom house, surrounded by all her stuff and essence. Some days, I swear I can smell her, hear her voice calling me to eat my Jollof rice and plantain, feel her hands on my shoulder shaking me awake for another day of work at the contact centre. In my dreams, I'm telling her that we're now rich, that she doesn't need to do her stressful night-shifts at the care home, nursing dementia patients and cleaning their mess-deluged arses.

Waking up to the reality of her permanent absence from my life is more than I can bear on most days, coupled with the guilt, the soul-killing guilt that steals my will to live. I can't forgive myself for the cruel words I spoke to Mum on countless occasions in my teenage years, blaming her for my father's absence, for my truancy, my smoking, my drinking, my fighting, my swearing, my shoplifting, my loitering and every delinquency I recall from my teenage days.

I weep for my careless acceptance of her selfless love, the big mansion I never bought for her, the self-esteem I never returned to her heart by making it big in life, and most of all, for all the money that I now possess as a result of her death, blood money, Mum's sacrifice and blood. Even though I know she'll be happy for me to have the money, this freaking and unexpected windfall, it doesn't stop the guilt, the resentment and the self-loathing that shrouds me with misery.

Shaniq says I should sell Mum's house and buy a house for us now that we can afford it outright. But, I can't seem to drag myself out of this house I shared with my mum. My extended compassionate leave from work has now become a permanent resignation as I try to work through the sense of hopelessness that engulfs me when I awake to each new dawn without Mum.

Shaniq isn't happy with me, I sense her impatience and frustration but she's not the one that's lost her mum. She has a large family with two parents, together with a sister, brothers and cousins. She can afford to lose one of them and carry on with her life. All I had was Mum and now, I have nothing.

I'm ashamed of my weakness, the inertia that grips me, killing my motivation. When Shaniq tries to move into Mum's house with me, I refuse. I feel it's disrespectful to Mum and Shaniq thinks I'm disrespectful to her. She hasn't visited or spoken to me in almost a week and I fear she may never see me again. Should that happen, on top of everything, I fear I may do something drastic. Thankfully, Shaniq relents but on one condition—that I undergo bereavement counselling. I resist her pressure for a long time, as I don't want anyone to think I'm weak or crazy or some other kind of shite. Africans don't do shrinks, I tell her. I mean, what can I say to a white person or some black stranger about my problems? Next thing you know, your medical record's all screwed up and your career prospects or political ambitions all but ruined. No, but no, thank you.

But Shaniq is deaf to my "No", and is like a mosquito in my ears till finally, I cave in. I sneak into my appointment with Karen Dunphy, a sweet middle-aged Irish woman who combines standard shrinking with some new age, woo-woo stuff. She's talking mind and energy, spirit guides, crystals and meditation, together with prescribed science and logic. Within minutes, she makes me forget her colour and my ignorant prejudice. By the end of our first session, I sign on for the long haul.

My road to recovery and redemption is a slow and painful process but Shaniq sticks with me through the long, gruelling ride. In the end, under Karen Dunphy's expert and compassionate guidance, I'm able to release all the poison killing my soul. I also release Mum into the loving arms of Jesus Christ, where I know she would wish to be. I'm almost free of my bad debts of guilt and shame, and I no longer dream of Mum's crushed and bloodied face every night. And I've now decided to put the house in the market. Shaniq and I have already viewed a few houses and hope to start our family as soon as we complete. We want four kids, three girls and a boy. I already plan to name one of our daughters Yinka, after Mum.

*

I'm packing up my stuff for vacant possession when I notice I've run out of boxes to put my stuff. I decide to pick some boxes from the corner shop. I'm cool with the guys that run the shop and can have as many boxes as I need from their back yard. I soon collect a couple of boxes and, on a whim, buy a Euro lottery ticket for the evening's play. No idea why I bought the ticket, save for the fact that it's something I used to do when Mum lived, when I yearned for a win to free us from our desperate poverty. Now, I'm a millionaire with enough money to meet my needs and some, I no longer need a lottery ticket. But old habits can be hard to break, and anyway, a win won't be unwelcome if it happens. Fat chance, though. I'm still smiling as I dump the boxes into Sky Blue's boot. In no time, I ease into our driveway and kill the engine. I unload the boxes and carry them towards the front door.

Just as I insert the key into the lock, I hear a soft thud and turn around. A cold chill spreads over my body, layering my skin with goosebumps. The pigeon is perched atop Sky Blue's roof, its black-rimmed eyes staring at me with the familiar malevolent glitter I've come to recognise.

The boxes drop from my jellied hands, crashing on the front garden slabs. My head is constricting and expanding as I stare at the pigeon. Thoughts are running wild inside my head, memories awakened from a deep and forgotten place inside me. I saw this pigeon on the day of my accident, the day I permanently lost two of my front teeth. I saw it again on the day of Mum's accident, the day she died. I feel my breath coming in short, fast gasps. Come on, man; get a grip. It's just a bloody pigeon, a fat stinking pigeon, that's all. Stuff happens. Just a freaking coincidence. Don't go imagining superstitious shite like Mum.

I'm shaking my head violently, as if I can shake away the vile bird from my sight. But...but... why is it always this same pigeon out of all the hundreds of pigeons that live in this street? I never saw it before I bought Sky Blue. It's as if it just hates my car, as if the mere sight of Sky Blue's gleaming body enrages the dirty sod. I feel a sudden rage replace my terror, red hatred beyond anything I've ever experienced drenching my skin in sudden hot sweat. If I had a gun, the wretched bird would be a goner in a blink.

I glare at the pigeon, determined to stare it down. Stuff it! We're done, mate! I ain't chasing you no more. Shit as much as you like and see if I give an ant's piss. It's as if the pigeon hears my thoughts because it does the familiar gross twitch of its bum and drops its stinky white bomb on my car roof. I feel a rush of adrenalin, fuelled by rage but resist the urge to shout and wave my arms as before. As I turn to pick up my boxes, I catch a movement from the corner of my eyes, a slight swish of feathered arse. I don't need to look to know that Sky Blue's bonnet has just been baptised with pigeon goo. The vile bird flies up to my neighbour's roof and stares down at me with smug glee, its eyes, little hard marbles of pure evil.

"Go ahead, you freaking, fat shite-arse!" I yell at it, giving it the middle finger before I unlock the front door. "Shit as much as you like and see if I give a shite. Ha! If I give a shite. One of these days, some saint's going to squash you under the tyres of his car, and I'll be dancing on your filthy carcass, you stinky shitbag. I hope you die a very painful death."

I walk into the house and slam the door behind me. My heart is still pounding as I head into the kitchen and pour myself a glass of Prosecco. I try to put away all thoughts of the wretched bird, but a strange, restless dread grips me, an elusive feeling, a sense of foreboding so strong my entire body breaks out in cold sweat.

I try to continue with my packing but I'm too jittery. I switch on the telly, scroll through channels in search of something gripping to hold my attention and kill the strange mood that holds me in its jittery thrall.

Somehow, I find myself on the lottery channel. The balls are rolling, and the numbers are coming up. I remember I purchased a ticket at the corner shop and reach into the pockets of my jeans to withdraw my ticket. It's all rumbled and mingy but I can still see the numbers clearly. The first number is a match; then the second, and third. A flicker of excitement ignites my heart. By the time they get to the fourth number, I'm quivering with tension. A sense of wonderment suddenly overwhelms me and goosepimples layer my skin. Even before the bonus number is called out, I know... I just know I already hold the winning ticket to twenty-eight million freaking, sweet British pounds sterling in my hands! Yaah Babes! Is this good luck or IS THIS FREAKING GOOD LUCK?

I jump up and down, let out several loud hoots of joy, scratch my head with trembling hands and fall on my knees as the enormity of my win hits me. I can't stop smiling, cackling like a lunatic tripping on some weird Ganja. I'm itching to share my news with the world and I'm just about to call Shaniq and tell her we've struck gold when my mobile rings. I grab it from the side table without checking the caller ID. Anyone will do to share my incredible news with. I mean, this kind of good luck is a one-in-a-million-lifetime kind of luck. Oh yaah Babes!

The voice I hear on the phone is one that's familiar, yet, strange. It quivers with suppressed tears. I feel a sudden tight racing of my heart, a hard pounding in my head. My joy vanishes as if an invisible hand has switched off a light bulb. A roaring voice inside my head tells me to cut off the call, end it before the caller can deliver her message. But my hand is frozen on the devise, pressing it tighter against my ear.

"Ade," the voice cries my name, a voice I now recognise as Shaniq's sister, Lekisha. "Ade... Ade... it's Shaniq. Shaniq is dead!

She's dead, Ade; my sister is dead! Oh my God, why? Why?" Lekisha is sobbing as her words reverberate inside my head like the thunderous blasts of a million killing bombs. I can't remember how the rest of the call goes or how it ends. I remember nothing else except the loud roaring in my head, a fatalistic resignation to its glass-eyed curse, as I feel myself falling, drowning in the sticky white sea of pigeon poo.

*

I stroke the new beard on my face with fingers that shake from a steady overdose of black coffee and nicotine. The living room stinks of cigarette smoke and unwashed body. I push away the insidious thought that says I smell like a living corpse, a man whose time is up but still clings desperately to a life that's no longer his own. I am a prisoner in my mother's house, a doomed man who must never sleep, must stay sentinel over the fireplace boarded up with trays, cushions, and anything else I can use to seal if off, including Mum's heavy fabric chair. Nothing must get through that fireplace, not while there's still breath in me to fight.

I haven't stepped out of the house in the two weeks since Shaniqua died at the hands of a drugged mugger with a knife. I hear my mobile phone ringing, over and over; hear the occasional knocks on the door and my name called through the letter box— friends, well-wishers, Shaniq's family, courier delivery drivers. I ignore them and huddle on the sofa, still in the same jeans and black polo shirt I was wearing when the phone rang on that fateful day of doom. They send the police to check on me, my caring good friends and neighbours. But I send the police away with my faked cheerful voice behind my locked door. They think I just need to take a break from everything, and they leave me alone in my brick prison.

I curse myself for my stupidity that day, for failing to see the writing on the wall or rather, the shite on the car. I should've known when I won the lottery that something else would have to be sacrificed for my good luck. That's how that evil bird of omen works, a bird I now know I willed into my life with my burning desire for wealth, together with its cursed metallic-blue accomplice. Mum was right. Sky Blue is indeed the devil's ride and that accursed fat pigeon is the devil himself.

Even as I watch the sealed fireside, I know that the black-eyed demon is outside waiting for me on Sky Blue's roof, waiting to glare good luck and worse misfortune into my soul if I'm ever stupid enough to leave the safety of the house. Ying-Yang, fortune and misfortune, good and bad, night and day; that's how all omens work, positive or negative. Except, the accursed bird has brought me the full Monty, every omen in its arsenal, the good, the bad and the pure evil. It's given me everything I desired and taken everything I love from me. Now, it has no use for me, and I fear it's come for my life; time for me to pay up for my diabolical purchase.

I hear its steady hoots coming down the chimney as I crouch on the sofa. In all my years of existence in Mum's house, I've never heard a pigeon's hoot in our chimney – not once. But now, it's there, day and night, a ghastly dirge that seeks my soul. Last night, I must've nodded off briefly because I recall a dream, Mum's urgent voice telling me to get rid of Sky Blue without delay. She said that gleaming car of my dreams brought the evil bird along with it and that I must rid myself of the car to rid myself of the pigeon and its curse. I wake up shaking, waiting for dawn to break the night skies, for that vile bird to permanently leave the narrow tunnel of my chimney for wherever evil realm it was originally spawned.

The agent from WeScrapAnyCar.Com is coming to collect Sky Blue for scrapping. I fear that his greed might not let him scrap her when he sees her beautiful body and hears her seductive, purring engine. I don't care what he does as long as he drives that bitch away from my house. No way I'm I stepping out of this house while that accursed car is parked outside our house and remains in my possession.

I hear a loud knock on the door and make a dash for the narrow hall. Even as I'm confirming the agent's name through the letterbox, I hear the other sound, the frantic scratching, pecking, and maniacal hoots coming from the barricaded fireside. It's as if it knows, as if the feathered demon is determined to get through to me before its car is sold. I push the car key through the letterbox to the agent and rush back into the living room, pushing back the heavy fabric chair which has impossibly been shifted from the fireside. Just in time! My heart is thumping, and my breathing is harsh and rushed. I hear the frustrated cry behind the chimney wall that sounds more human than bird, the voice of something very old and cold. It chills me to the bone, bringing the shivers to my body.

Then, I hear it scramble up the chimney as the agent revs the car engine to test it before buying. I wipe the sweat from my face with weariness and await the next assault, fearing this time, I might not be strong enough to withstand its supernatural attack. The agent knocks at the door once again and asks if I'm sure this is the car I want to scrap. His voice is as incredulous as I expect. He shouts a quote through the letterbox, but I tell him the car is free, that it's cursed. His stunned silence speaks more than any shrink's diagnoses. But he wouldn't be a good salesman if he doesn't sense an easy kill and hunt it down with ruthless zeal.

We finally agree on fifty quid, since he says he must pay me something to legalise the sale. I sense his glee at the bargain he thinks he's struck, convinced he's dealing with a hundred-carat certified lunatic. Greed seeps from every pore in his body despite my desperate warning, the greed that feeds the malevolence of that accursed bird. As he pushes the cash through the letterbox, he laughs about a crazy pigeon that seems to have taken a fancy to my car and will not leave it.

"Has it got black rims around its eyes?" I ask. I need to be sure.

"Yeah! How did you know?" The agent laughs again. "Don't tell me you keep the pigeon as a pet," he jokes.

A cold chill runs down my spine as I hear the agent's words. I quickly push out the car registration papers, sign his forms, show my ID and hand over the spare key and manual. I explain I have chickenpox, hence our letterbox transaction. He commiserates and pushes my own copy of the forms through the handy letterbox, whistling cheerfully as he exits my front garden. Within seconds, I hear Sky Blue's distinctive purr as she's driven away from our street for good.

A heavy weight lifts from my shoulders, a dark shadow, the sense of doom that has held me bondage since the day Mum died. I take a deep breath and exhale noisily. It's gone! That evil bird of omen has finally left for good, following the corrupt reek of the beautiful blue hearse that brought it into my life! I draw my curtains and open my windows for the freshest air I've inhaled in over a week. Then, I take a long shower and shave my overgrown beard. I'm thinking later perhaps, I'll make my way to my barber to reclaim the designer baldness of my icon, the music rapper, COMMON.

Outside, I can hear the sounds of life, humanity and normalcy, horns, sirens, lawn mowers, ice-cream vans, children's squeals and adults' chatter. A low-flying plane drones overhead beneath the blue skies. Everything is bright and new and I too, I feel as fresh and new as a new-born infant. Thank you, Mum. Thank you for always being there for me, loving me, protecting me, even in death! Shaniq, I'm so, so sorry, Babes. Forgive me... please, forgive me...

The tears are building up again and my thoughts are going crazy inside my head like a million ants high on cocaine. Oh God, what if the scrap company doesn't scrap Sky Blue? What if someone else buys her and brings that cursed pigeon into their lives? That would make me a murderer, wouldn't it? Oh dear Lord, what to do, what to do?

I pick up my mobile phone and call Karen Dunphy.

ECHOES FROM THE PAST
(A Coventry Memory)

By Mary Ogilvie

Winding entries,
Dirty newspapers,
Scattered on the ground.
Now you see,
Now you don't,
Your childhood all around.

Before you grow up and dash away
Little do you know,
Of the peace
That you have left behind,
In the warmth
Of that old road.

You used to give her two shillings and six pence pocket money when she was a little girl with tumbling curls and grazed knees. She did not have to do much to earn your respect, only just be herself.

She used to sit on the wall outside your house and play with the children from round about. In the entries filled with scattered litter, they enjoyed the games of childhood: chasing, hiding, playing with marbles; and on the crooked flagstones they hopped and skipped and ran about until it was time to go in.

You used to laugh a lot then, Granddad, and your eyes shone through the smoke from your pipe as you told stories of your own childhood which she eagerly listened to.

Later on, as a young woman, she would knock the door, not so frequent then but you knew that she would come. Dressed in the latest fashions and wearing a painted face she would step inside, but again you would just see her. Now she told stories and you listened as you blew those grey circles from your pipe.

But nothing had changed. She would slip back in time and be the little girl who used to do the shopping and sat quietly still when the football results were announced on the television. You used to share your dinner with her, leaving a little on the side of the plate, and laughing she bathed in the warmth and joy of being loved.

The years slipped by, and when she said she was getting married, she did not remember much about your thoughts, but you were there in the midst of activities and still singing her praises. You shared that warmth again with her husband and when their family came along, it was there for them too.

Then her visits became more frequent. You were both growing older, and you were becoming frail. Your pipe you had put to one side, and your eyes still shone, but their light was growing dimmer. Now you both talked. Maturity had taught her many things. She brought the world to you and although your mind was still clear, you needed that assurance.

Now it was time to give all that love back to you, and in your slower years she tried to give you hope when your spirit was low. Sometimes she would find you sitting in the darkness, but a single glow from the fire would be bright enough, and that feeling of peace was to be a special memory.

Finally, you went into hospital, but you could still laugh even with those other mixed emotions. She held your hand and you both talked of the past. Time had allowed that. But your years were drawing to a close. Surrounded by your loved ones they each had their own memories to recall. Slowly you were going, and then you were gone.

It had been raining lightly the morning she knocked on the door of your house for the last time. The window was opened, and a gentle breeze played with the curtains. As she stepped inside, she could sense that you were no longer there, but then the sun came out and a beam of light filtered into the room. Its warmth radiated a feeling of peace which you once had shared, and as she bathed in its glow, she knew that chapter had finally come to its close.

Years later, as she stood at your graveside, she thought about this city, Coventry, which you once knew so well. Like you, it had moved on, but you would be amazed just how much it had risen again, like a Phoenix from the ashes, and was to become the City of Culture in the year 2021.

COVENTRY'S LADY GODIVA

By Ann Evans

A visit to Coventry would not be complete without discovering the city's most famous woman from history, Lady Godiva. A bronze statue in her honour stands at Broadgate, the heart of the city. Remains of the priory she founded back in 1043 are still visible for visitors to see and explore.

She has been the inspiration for poets, painters, sculptors and historians for a thousand years. Mentioned in the Domesday Book, she was one of the greatest women of her time – the fourth richest woman in England and grandmother to a future Queen of England. She was a pious and generous benefactor to the church and built what was to become the only cathedral that Henry VIII destroyed in the Dissolution of the Monasteries – Lady Godiva. And of course, her famous ride naked through the streets of Coventry is what people recall most about her.

Lady Godiva, or Godigfu – Gift of God, was very much a real person. One thousand years ago, at the time of King Cnut, Godiva married Leofric, Earl of Mercia, a powerful nobleman who owned a third of England, they had a son – Aelfgas. Some historians believe it was her second marriage, and that Hereward the Wake was also her son. A rich and powerful woman, Godiva was renowned for her beauty and her piety. She was a generous benefactor to many religious establishments, but she built her most beautiful church in Coventry.

Built on consecrated ground, on the site of a former religious house for nuns, St Mary's Priory Church with its one prior and 24 monks was consecrated in 1043 and later, in 1102 became Coventry's first cathedral. Godiva gave all her gold, silver and jewels to be made into ornamentation for her church which held the relics of two saints – the head of Saint Osburg and the arm of Saint Augustine. Such relics attracted pilgrims to Coventry bringing education and trade.

Lord Leofric died on 30 October 1057 and was buried in one of the church porches. Godiva outlived him a further ten years, she also outlived their son Aelfgas who died in 1062. Aelfgas' daughter however, grew up to marry Harold King of England, so for a while Godiva was grandmother to the future Queen of England.

Godiva herself died in 1067 and on her deathbed bequeathed her prayer beads which were made of jewels, to her church, and had them placed around the image of Mary holding the child Jesus, so that every pilgrim who passed would stop and say a prayer for each bead. She left behind a legacy of spirit and a legacy of faith – which has lived on into the 21st century.

As for that famous ride, there is no mentioned of it until 100 years after her death in the 'Flowers of History' by Roger of Wendover, a monk at St Albans Abbey. These monks were renowned for collecting news and stories from passing travellers.

The legend tells of how Godiva persuaded her reluctant husband, Earl Leofric, to reduce the tax burden on the townspeople of Coventry. In particular, the heregeld tax. He agreed to do so – but at a price. If she would ride naked through Coventry's marketplace at midday as a celebration of the perfection of God's work. He would in return, abolish all local taxes save those on horses. To his surprise she agreed.

On the appointed day, flanked by two fully clothed horsewomen, she rode naked through the market, straight in her saddle, with a composed expression, unashamed of her nudity. The taxes were duly removed.

Historians argue that this would never have happened. Lady Godiva was herself a powerful woman. If she'd wanted to reduce taxes she would have simply done so – in Saxon law, she had as much power as her husband. Additionally, the legend makes Leofric sound a grim, hard man, when in fact he was considered a saint in his time.

Some suggest that naked could have meant stripped of her finery. Others say the legend was nothing but a monkish tale.

As for the story of Peeping Tom – a local man who couldn't resist taking a peek at Godiva as she rode by and was subsequently struck blind, there is actually no mention of him in ancient manuscripts or records until the 17th century.

Monkish tale or truth, Godiva's story has lived on, and from the 17th century there have been Godiva processions and pageants. The first was in 1678 when Godiva was played by a boy as women and girls were not allowed to take part.

In 1862 Godiva was played by Madame Letitia, described as "fair, fat and at least forty", who almost fainted half-way around the procession due to the heat and the fact that she was overweight. She was revived in a public house with gin.

In the 20th century the city council paid for an actress to play Godiva – La Milo, an 'Artist of the Veils', who, it was said, would ride without her veils. News of this outrageous spectacle caused furious arguments and tremendous media coverage. An incredible 30,000 people turned out to watch the procession. Many, no doubt, went home disappointed, as La Milo kept on all of her veils.

In 1949 a bronze statue of Lady Godiva was created by Sir William Reid Dick. This stands in Broadgate at the heart of the City Centre as a reminder of this great lady.

Today, Coventry has its very own Lady Godiva. Pru Poretta, a mother of three and now a grandmother, took on the role in 1982 and has since become a true champion of the city.

Pru recalled that event, and how she actually made her horse blush. "I had made a burgundy-coloured velvet cape for the beautiful white horse I was to ride on, but a thunderstorm drenched the three-hour procession. When we removed the cape, the colour had run and the horse had turned pink – he was blushing!"

In 2009 Pru was made an MBE in the New Year's Honours List. She is quoted at the time as saying, "Godiva fought injustices and helped people work together. A lot of what I do today is helping to bring the community together."

Although she has made seven rides in Godiva pageants over the years, Pru's real work, like Godiva's is for the benefit of others. She regularly gives talks and tours, visits schools, hospitals and hospices. She tirelessly involves herself with community group projects and multi-cultural events. Making sure the story, the memory, the reality and the spirit of Lady Godiva lives on.

INCIDENT AT IKEA

By Owen Jennings

I had just walked through the revolving door at Ikea, Coventry. There I saw an old friend sitting in the cafe area. I joined him at his table. He looked at me blankly. I started a one-sided conversation.

Soon after, the manageress approached us. She asked if I knew the person I was sharing a table with. I told her I had known Pete before evolution was invented. She said he had trouble remembering where he had left his bicycle.

Pete replied he had been told to move his bike from his regular parking spot. So, he locked it up in a new location. That was the rub, he could not remember where that new place was.

After a long pause Pete said he was unsure if he cycled into the city centre in the first place. I pointed to the helmet on the table and the bicycle clips on his ankles and remarked one rarely wears items like that as a fashion statement.

Then it clicked. About two months earlier we'd met up at a birthday bash. I had told him about a herd of bullocks that had been put to graze in the flood meadow at the back of his house. He said the bullocks were a load of bollocks. Miffed, I told him to go home and look over his back fence.

He would see these big mooing things that chewed grass at one end and plopped cow pats at the other. By his reaction you would think I was telling him the Martians had landed. At that point I was grabbed by the elbow and a mate ushered me away. This mutual friend told me Pete had Alzheimer's.

"Do you mean Alka Seltzer?"

"No, that makes a glass of water go fizzy. Alzheimer's makes the mind go fuzzy. You suffer memory loss."

That was the reason for his anger. People with this form of dementia find it hard to deal with changes to their surroundings.

This was why I got to be sitting next to a guy who was confused about how he got to be where he sat. I thought it best to tell the manageress Pete was not his full self. I also wanted to do it in a way that did not embarrass him. So, I looked at her directly and mimed the phrase. Pete has got Alzheimer's."

She stared back at me totally puzzled. "What did you say, sir?"

I raised my voice to a whisper. "Pete's got Alzheimer's."

"You will have to speak up, sir."

This was no lip-reading lady. I gave up being tactful and shouted out so the whole world could hear. "He's got Alzheimer's."

Pete looked around the cafe. He wanted to get a good look at the person I was talking about. His reaction flustered the manageress. She took out her mobile and phoned for the police.

Ten minutes later a cycling constable turned up. He came through the large revolving door pushing his bicycle.

Pete cheered up. "You have found my bike!"

"No sir, this is West Midland Police property."

Pete glared at the officer with suspicion. He scanned the bike for tell-tale signs that it was really his.

I used his distraction to whisper to the Constable that Pete had Alzheimer's disease. My resumed tact was on account I assumed my friend would have forgotten the earlier shouting out.

The policeman sat down so he was between the bike and Pete. He was taking no chances of Pete making a mad dash for the bicycle and riding off on it. "Can you describe your bike, sir?"

"Just like yours, Constable."

"Come off it, sunshine. Your bike would not have police logos plastered all over it."

"It is a mountain bike. The same model you have, Constable."

"You have left it somewhere in this vicinity, sir?"

"I am not sure, Officer."

"Can you tell me who was the Prime Minister during the Second World War?" asked the policeman.

"The name started with a C," said Pete. He spoke with a wry smile. "Chamberlain. There was another one and his name started with a C. Clement Attlee."

"So, I am dealing with a clever-clogs."

I intervened to tell the officer Pete was a fully qualified engineer who gained his City and Guilds at the Butts College.

The Constable squared up to Pete. "What did you do this morning, sir?"

"Sorry officer. I don't have a clue."

The Constable then questioned me. Just to make sure he did not have a job lot on his hands.

"This is not a police matter. Your friend needs medical help," said the Constable. He called for an ambulance. Then he went outside to wait for it to turn up.

While we sat there Pete decided to take a leak. The gents' door was in my sight line, so I thought it was safe for him to go off on his own. As I sat there, I saw the ambulance drive up. The medics got out. They spoke to the police officer. The Constable pointed through the window at our table. Then he got on his bike and cycled off.

The ambulance men entered the store and approached me. "Are you alright sir?"

"I am fine."

"We are here to take you to Walsgrave Hospital."

"You have got the wrong person."

"There is nothing to worry about, sir. Let us help you up."

These Medics were big blokes. I found myself being carefully but firmly led off to the exit. Pete came out of the toilet. On seeing my friend, I struggled to break loose. The medics kept me in their grip.

"He is the man you want," I shouted. "Tell them Pete."

The medics stopped. "Do you know this person?" asked the larger Medic.

A serene Pete observed the struggling me with a benign bemusement. "I am sorry, gentlemen. I have never seen that man before in my life."

For my own protection I was strapped down in the ambulance. I saw through the open back door the IKEA manageress and Pete. They had stepped out onto the forecourt. She had found his bicycle. He put on his helmet, shook her hand, gave me a wave. Then he got on his bicycle and cycled off.

LIFE UNDERGROUND

By Maxine Burns

Binley colliery was opened in 1907 by Merry and Cunningham, coal mine owners from Glasgow and for the next sixty years it stood proud, smouldering and ominous, a heaven or hell, depending on who remembers it.

An early report defines the miners as, 'a generally healthy, tall, athletic and powerful race of men, continuing their labour to an advanced age,' although the report goes on to describe an 'extremely poor and scant diet,' which seems curiously at odds with this portrayal. However, the men, engineers and miners, settled in well and the first coal was mined in 1910.

In the late 1920s the colliery went into liquidation and was taken over by The Binley Colliery company and the workforce was rapidly expanded. The depression which had overtaken Britain, forced many to flee their homes in search of work, some in the coal mines, others to the growing motor industries - the Midlands being one of few areas with such vacancies.

The local neighbourhood was significantly transformed. Families made their way to Binley from around the country, largely from Scotland, particularly Glasgow, complete with accents incomprehensible to many of the local populace. Homes were built to house the increasing workforce and the miner's organised their own communities. A cooperative store was founded, as was a band, complete with male voice choir.

A park for the children was soon followed by a bowling green and tennis court, all maintained and paid for by the miners themselves. They received a free coal allowance of 600 kilos per month, delivered to the house by horse and cart. These must have been splendid activities to indulge in after the hardships of their working week.

The shift began with a journey to another world, in a cage descending many metres in practically freefall. Grim faced, packed tight and holding their breath on an authentic white-knuckle ride, a cacophony of noise awaited them as they spilled out of the cages at the pit head. Amidst the throbbing engines, humming fans and hissing steam the men faced many dangers. Accidents were frequent and many were killed or maimed.

Warwickshire coal was especially prone to spontaneously ignite and if left unchecked, fire could spread rapidly. Carbon monoxide leaking into the atmosphere was the main cause of fatalities, a constant, invisible workmate.

The miners laboured in cramped, back breaking conditions, their coal blackened faces streaked with sweat, breathing in deadly dust in a dark, hot hell. The machinery that would make their working lives more tolerable came much later.

Conditions improved when the coal industry was nationalised in 1947. Outdated machinery was modernised and bathing facilities, a long-held aspiration by the workers, were at last installed.

In the early 1960s the mining industry was, as a whole in decline. Closures were imminent and although at Binley reserves were far from exhausted, mining ceased. Across the country communities were left devastated by the disappearance of the working pits, the loss of income, the comradery, a whole way of life which had been passed down from father to son for generations. It vanished almost overnight and despite the hardships involved, many remember those days with fondness and regret.

The men at Binley were luckier than most as other industries remained close by for the miners to retrain.

Binley colliery finally closed in 1963. It is now an important wildlife area, managed by Warwickshire Wildlife trust and cared for by local volunteers. Claybrookes Marsh Nature Reserve, as it is now known, has been designated a site of special scientific interest, due to the population of rare insects it supports. Opened in 1999, it is named for Jack Clay and James Brookes, two of three miners killed by a roof fall in July 1947. It acts as a memorial to all miners killed at the pit over the years.

Note:

Britain's last deep coal mine, North Yorkshires Kellingley Colliery closed in 2015.

STARDUST

By Paul Monks

"So, you want to be a photographer?" she asked.

"Yes," I replied. "And I was told when I joined this scheme that there was a possible placement with the Coventry Evening Telegraph."

"Mmmm," she replied, scanning her notes. "Well, I don't know who told you that, but we can't place you with them. Have you thought about working in Woolworths? We can get you a placement on the pick-n-mix stall. It's quite near to the photobooth, so it's really relevant."

The last bit of that is, clearly, a fabrication; but it didn't feel like it at the time. It felt pretty much like it was – a scheme to keep kids off the unemployment figures for a bit longer and for companies in the area to get some cheap temporary workers.

I was just 17 years of age and into my second year on a Youth Training Scheme, which was where they sent every school leaver of no fixed ability in those days. I'd joined the Searchlight Centre at Cardinal Newman School aged 16, still as wet behind the ears as an over-eager puppy. There I'd discovered pop music, fallen deeply into unrequited love and tried my best to become a photographer on the rather shaky grounds that I'd somehow won a couple of competitions as a kid.

But now here I was, in the old Alfred Herbert factory with all the friends I had made in the previous year scattered to the winds and with no real hope that they would place me anywhere other than the factory floor that had been silently looming in my future since Mr Lole had told me a year earlier that: "I'm not going to enter you for your photography exam; you won't pass and I can't be bothered with the paperwork."

Sylvia, the placement officer, looked at me with eyes that betrayed a long dead soul. "Well, there is one option," she said.

There was a pause, and she examined her papers again as if not really sure. "There's a placement at The Belgrade Theatre in the lighting and sound department. There's lighting in photography and there's lighting in theatre so it's really appropriate..." And that one, my friend, I'm not making up.

The job of the Lighting & Sound (LX – short for Lighting & Effects) Department is quite simple really. During the run up to a show it is their job to plan and install the lighting rig, often risking life and limb by standing on the edge of the private boxes with a heavy follow spot in one hand and a frayed electric cable in the other, whilst making sure never to leave anything on the stage after two pm lest the carpentry department paint over it on their way back from the mid-day pub break that started the previous Wednesday.

Once the run of the show begins it is their job to maintain the lights, fight to the death each night with the antiquated control board, obey the various sound and lighting cues and, most importantly, make sure that the lead actors are happy with the sound and lights at all times. Woe betide anyone who accidentally leaves someone in shadow during their pivotal line. Finally, of course, once the show is finished it is their job to take everything down and re-rig ready for the next show, which can often be later the same day.

It's a hard job with long unsociable hours, lots of running around, no breaks and barely any pay but it's still probably the most fun I've ever had in the workplace. Having access to the secret, backstage world of the theatre, sitting in the green room and chatting with the actors, feeling the jingle of all those keys to hidden rooms at your belt, I'd happily go back there tomorrow.

During my time at the theatre there was a whole run of mostly forgettable plays from Lock Up Your Daughters (a terrible period farce), The Elephant Man, Jingle Jangle Jungle, a touring version of Wuthering Heights with a Heathcliffe who insisted on bellowing every line and was therefore, unintentionally,

115

hilarious; and a whole set of one-off performances from travelling artists. But the only two shows that stick out in my mind are The Asylum and Godspell.

The Asylum featured the star of the movie 'Ryan's Daughter" Sarah Miles, as one of a small band of inmates at an asylum that was due to be demolished shortly after a failing pop-star filmed a video for his song, 'The Asylum' there. It was pretty dreadful stuff, standing out largely in the memory because Sarah insisted on staying at the most expensive hotel in Coventry meaning that the production ended up losing money. And secondly because the producer of the show decided to use a Robert Cray album as interval music. This was my first real introduction to the blues and made sitting through the show night after night almost bearable. My role was on the sound desk and with the help of the sound cues, it was my job to fade in and out the various tractor noises (for demolition), music cues (for the 'video' being recorded) and other related effects.

The show played to a mostly empty auditorium, with numerous gaps between softly dozing paying customers. After the first night we received a complaint and a request to turn one of the tractor sounds down as it had inadvertently woken someone up. But probably the hardest days' work of my life was done on the day of the fit-up for Godspell.

Early one Monday morning, far earlier than lighting and sound engineers would usually emerge from their beds, a series of big removal trucks arrived at the stage door of The Belgrade Theatre. There was a section of the wall that opened like a retracting shed door allowing entry through to the stage and from here we unloaded row after row of lighting rigs on metal frames and carried them to the stage where they were attached to pullies and winched up into place.

I spent all morning and most of the afternoon going backwards and forwards from the truck before climbing into the highest sections of the ceiling and helping to re-plug the lights, fetch coloured plastics and finally stand on the stage pointing the remote control (freshly painted over by the stage hands) in an attempt to try the lights at their different powers.

The first show was that same evening so there was no time to mess around as I clung precariously to the poles and tried not to look down at the treacherous drop below. Most theatres in those days hosted a mixture of self-produced and touring shows. Some would stay for a week, others for only an afternoon. There would be a sum total of eight shows of Godspell (Matinees on Wednesday and Saturday) before it moved on to the next town.

The show was a musical, telling the story of Jesus, much like the more successful Jesus Christ Superstar, only without the bad hair, and starred fading pop star and former green-cross code man Alvin Stardust (biggest hit: My Coo Ca Choo), who had himself recently found God and been born again. Born Bernard Jewry he had gone through a number of name changes and packs of Brylcreem before returning to the stage in a variety of different roles and was, even then, something of a crowd puller.

My main role for the show was to act as Stage Left Follow-spot (stage left and right being described from the point of view of someone standing on stage looking out at the audience) and to receive mocking comments from the audience in the breaks because of the black leggings I had to wear to become 'invisible' next to the spot. A follow spot is a very hot light that usually stands on a tripod in an unused audience box or cordoned off area and can be aimed and moved around to follow an actor at key points. The Spot is focused with an aperture that has to be checked to be loose enough to be moved quickly between queues so that it can cover practically the whole stage or single face. It may, from time to time, also be focused on the audience.

Mine had long since lost its targeting mechanism and had a thin line of earth-wire from a plug coiled around the barrel with one end twisted into a small cross-hair that could, at the expense of a very hot cheek, be looked down and adjusted to suit the individual operator. Each spot-operator also had three or four sheets of A4 paper with cues written on that were all but invisible once the auditorium lights were off.

Aside from the occasional 'funny' remark from an audience member and sweating like a pig during the show due to the small sun pressed tight against my left ear, I spent most of my time between shows and in intervals either repairing or adjusting lights that had been caught by an over-enthusiastic performer or sitting in the green-room (back stage break out canteen room, none of which is ever actually even remotely green), having cups of tea that a nice lady called Vi made from a large metal urn, and crashing out on a series of sofas that had long since lost whatever spring had been built into them.

It was in this room one day, whilst sipping a drink that might have been tea three days previously but was now just a brown liquid that was showing early signs of intelligent life, that I saw my first real example of bigotry when the actor playing Judas ran in, hotly pursued by a ranting and raving lead actor.

'You'll burn in hell,' Stardust was screaming, 'God damn you.' Judas was, by now, in floods of tears as the other man called him every name he could think of and called for his eternal damnation because, as a born again Christian, Stardust viewed the other man's homosexuality as a sin against God. Oddly, I think that may have been one of the early things that has made me a passionate supporter of LGBTQ rights.

I don't remember how the argument ended. I think the actor playing Judas shut himself away in his room. Someone may have gone to comfort him. Thinking back, I can't imagine what that must have been like for him, knowing that there were still so many stops for the show before it would end.

The only other thing I remember about the show was that Alvin didn't half milk his death scene for all he could. He could probably have started a dairy it was that bad.

As you will know the story of Jesus ends with him on the cross, dying for all mankind, only to be resurrected and I don't know if it was just me, but that death scene seemed to get a little longer every night. This was back before I had learned to drive and I was solely reliant on the last bus to get me home, so I would be nervously eyeing my watch as the moment arrived.

The entire stage would go into complete and growing darkness with only one spot, mine, on the lead actor. As the fatal moment came, I had to narrow the light and keep it focused on his face, meaning that I couldn't lock it into position and had to hold it steady despite the heat and the weight. By the last few words only his eyes, nose and mouth would be visible in the darkness as Alvin began to sing

"Ohh Go-od." The music was muted, only the solitary sound of a sombre piano. "I'm dy-i-ing." A long pause. Alvin's eyes would lift to the heavens as if for some reprieve. By now my hands would be beginning to shake.

"Oh.........Go-o-od," an even longer pause, a sob and the light leaking into my eye from the side of the barrel and creating a halo, "I'm....dy-i-i-i-i-i-i-i-i-i-ing."

There was almost total silence in the packed theatre. Not a pin could be heard to drop, not a shuffle of feet to drown out Alvin's increasingly thick slices of ham. Total silence reigned and only those with the sharpest of hearings could possibly have picked out the sound of me muttering under my breath for him to just get the hell on with it and die already.

"Oh G-od," one last sigh, "I'm dead."

That was it. That was my cue. Follow spot snaps off, quickly adjust the aperture, a swell of music and five minutes later the audience still haven't finished clapping as I'm tearing out of the theatre and running to jump on the bus just as it pulls around the corner.

At the end of the week there was, of course, a clear up exercise, but I was away due to a family party, so I never got to see the rigging being packed away into the vans, nor the stars check out of their digs. A few months later my placement came to an end and despite being kept on for the panto, there was no permanent job available. I would go on to do a small bit of amateur theatre a few years later but other than that and the occasional trip to see a show, my time at the Belgrade theatre has been limited.

When I do go there though I always take a moment to glance back at the hidden room where the lighting and sound team sit in darkness, and to glance up at the boxes and see if there is a follow spot operator there. It's not a glamorous life. No one in theatre will ever be rich. They will find their lives full of hard work and unsociable hours, often stuck with terrible plays showing to a half empty auditorium or dealing with temperamental, or just plain mental, cast members, but a part of me still envies them. Show business, there's nothing like it.

COVENTRY 2121: CELEBRATE WITH A BANG

By Gwydion M. Williams

And finally, a peek into the next century and an idea of the city's plans a hundred years hence.

Dear sister

I trust the weather on Mars is now behaving itself.

Yes, I am Chair for the Coventry 2121 celebrations. Confidentially, here is how it shapes.

Obviously, we look back to our famous 2021 City of Culture celebration. Not always reverently – a 'Dance of the Tower Blocks' shows how the City Council in that Coolheart era spoiled the famous Three Spires skyline. But I insisted on a 'mocker of mockers' to step in and remind them that they were not bad for that era – well above average.

But I've tried to avoid blandness. Dare sometimes to be negative. Even about our locally-sourced poet Phillip Larkin, and maybe bitching is the best way to commemorate him. There is a whole cycle saying what a lovely fellow he was, but separately there will be alternative views. One that I briefed a friend to do – keep that confidential. To be called From Hell and Hull and Phillip Larkin, Good Lord Deliver Us. Likewise, a mock-trial for alleged crimes against humanity and good humour: but let both sides be heard. And a jury morphed to look like kangaroos: run of the mill holography, I am assured. But that will just be one strand. His fans also get some generous support. That will keep them quiet, or rather keep them singing our tune.

We've flatly refused participation by some fundamentalist Aztecs. Even if modern medicine can remake you good as new after your heart has been ripped out, it is not in the spirit of Coventry as we see it. And some other ideas that I think you'd find distasteful rather than funny – assuming that is still within your range of humour.

We are allowing some rather tasteful fertility rites featuring Lady Godiva doing what she's famous for, and a few things more. Things a lady at the top of the late Saxon aristocracy certainly never did in real life. They were Christians of a couple of centuries standing, and had she madly wanted to go out naked in public, her husband would either have had her shut up in a nunnery or given her whatever she wanted. Still, the legend is much more fun. As is the comic version, which ends with the blinding of a villain called Thomas the Tank Engine. The local fans are getting their own event, so I hope tolerance will prevail. But not extending to bloodshed.

More controversially, we are allowing some silly Neo-Pagans to stage a Ragnarok re-enactment, adjusted to make it less violent and more of a fun event. We have a significant Neo-Pagan minority who can and have voted as a block, so they have to have something. And with all of these we say, if it is not your thing then stay away. A few years back we sponsored a Gynandromorph Festival, after all, even though most including myself ignored it. It was a record trading weekend, so it must have had its fans and many more curious onlookers.

Quite the opposite applies to re-enacting scenes from Tolkien's Smith of Wootton Major. Not one negative reaction, though many didn't care. But selecting 24 good children out of our broadly law-abiding population could have been a nightmare. I had a brainwave – let candidates be voted on by a selective electorate of anyone aged between 4 and 11 back in 2021.

Most of the rest will be the standard stuff. But I would single out an exhibition of 2121 Bacterial Cultures. Odd but cheap. Some edible.

And the big event? Our own comet, but not like most. They were a brilliant success in China's big 150-year celebration back in 2099. Borrowed a few from the dozens that are being used to

122

make a temporary biosphere on the EarthMoon. Had them glowing brightly all over China, and naturally seen by everyone else in the same latitude. But they have since been over-used. You'll not have seen them on Mars, I suppose. But with tight-zone street lighting, everyone appreciates the Milky Way that the 20th century lost. A huge intrusive comet often offends. And they are a cliché.

But we will be different. I have a friend at Peterborough Spaceport, where they have developed a variant, but want a trial run for their big celebration. The plan – which might not come off – is to bounce a comet off the troposphere. That should mean we get a decent meteoric effect and an amazing 'night of light'. And they figure it can be done safely. It may not happen but will be remarkable if it comes off.

Could you think maybe of coming home for it?

Alex Bartlett first came to Coventry University in 2002 from rural Surrey and has made his life and career in the Midlands with his writing-loving wife. Alex dreamt of writing from childhood, but got side-tracked by adult things like football, beer and requirement for a roof over his head to prevent the aforementioned beer becoming saturated with rain. Now the roof is over his head, and his wife does most of the cooking in exchange for him washing up, he's discovered he has more time for thinking up stories (especially when scrubbing the roasting dish clean) and getting some of them on paper.

*

Taffi Nyawanza is originally from Zimbabwe. He is a human rights lawyer and writer. He was a National Flash Flood Best of the Net 2020 nominee. His short fiction has appeared in various places, including Afritondo Journal; PerHappened mag, Kreaxxxion Review, Lumiere, Time to Breathe Journal.

Untitled: Voices Journal, Kalahari Journal, the National Flash Fiction Journal, Palewell Press and MIROnline. His manuscript of short stories was shortlisted by The St. Lawrence Book Award 2020. He was on the Exiled Writers Ink 2020 programme and published a chapbook with them titled 'The Men Who Have No Knees'.

His twitter handle is @tnyawanza and his website is Taffi.Nyawanza.co.uk

*

Emilie Lauren Jones has performed at a variety of events and venues across the UK and Ireland. Published in Under the Radar Magazine, HCE Magazine and Riggwelter, and anthologies including: *The View from Olympia* (Half Moon Books), *Bloody Amazing* (Beautiful Dragons Collaborations and Yaffle Press) and *Places of Poetry: Mapping the Nation in Verse* (One World Publications).

A strong believer that art and creativity are for everyone, she is passionate about making poetry accessible to a wide audience, this is reflected in the projects and commissions she takes part in.

One of the commissioned poets and Community Connector for UK City of Culture 2021, Emilie runs regular writing workshops for adults and young people, she also enjoys visiting schools and community groups to share her love of words.

She is Poet in Residence for Hillz FM, and in 2020, she represented her city in the Coventry-Cork Poetry exchange. She holds an MA in Creative Writing from the University of Birmingham and is part of the 2020/21 Nine Arches Press 'Dynamo' scheme.

www.emilielaurenjones.co.uk Social Media: @emilielaurenxxx

*

David Court – David Court is a short story author and novelist, whose works have appeared in over a dozen venues including *Tales to Terrify, StarShipSofa, Visions from the Void, Sparks, Burdizzo Mix Tape Volume One* and *Corona-Nation Street*. Whilst primarily a horror writer, he also writes science fiction, poetry and satire. His last collection, *Scenes of Mild Peril*, was re-released in 2020 and his debut comic writing has just featured in Tpub's *The Theory (Twisted Sci-Fi)*.

As well as writing, David works as a Software Developer and lives in Coventry with his wife, three cats and an ever-growing beard. David's wife once asked him if he'd write about how great she was. David replied that he would, because he specialized in short fiction. Despite that, they are still married.

Website: www.davidjcourt.co.uk
Twitter: @DavidJCourt

Ella Cook Ella's been obsessed with books since she was a toddler. She decided to become a writer as soon as she realised that stringing letters together in the right order could actually be a career. She grew up in the outskirts of London, where fairies lived at the bottom of her Grandma's garden, so it isn't surprising that she still looks for magic in everyday life – and often finds it.

When she's not living in a fantasy world of her own creation, she writes bids and develops programmes for children's services. She lives in a rural Midlands village (where there are probably more fairies) with her husband who is ever loving and understanding and makes her gallons of tea in magical cups that can keep drinks warm for whole chapters. She's a member of the Coventry Writer's Group and the SWWJ. and has won numerous awards for her fiction and poetry. Her debut novel, Beyond Grey, was published by Ruby Fiction (part of the Choc-Lit family) in January 2021 and picked up bestseller flags in 4 territories. She's thrilled with the reviews and feedback so far, and already working on her second and third books - with a few more in the pipeline.

You can contact Ella at ella.cook@outlook.com or find her on Twitter @Ellacookwrites

*

Bev Woodley works part time at a library and full time at becoming a writer. Her writing successfully won her a place at the 2016 WriteNow Birmingham event organised by Penguin Random House. This is her second published short story.

*

Maxine Burns writes articles, short fiction, plays and poetry. Her published work includes having a play performed at the Blue/Orange Theatre in Birmingham, and was a winner in the Coventry Peace Festival poetry competition. She is currently working on a novel about a village populated by dark, dysfunctional families. Maxine is a member of The Society of

Women Writers & Journalists (SWWJ) and is currently Chair of the Coventry Writers' Group. A position she has held on a number of occasions over the years.

*

Margaret Egrot blogs regularly about authors, writing, and the origins of words. She is the author of two novels for teenagers and a number of short stories for adults, including a collection of stories about the imagined off-stage lives of female characters in Shakespeare's plays. Most of her stories are available on Amazon. At least one story is always free and all the books are free on Kindle Unlimited. Margaret has also written a number of prize-winning short plays.

You can find her blog, books, and other information from the links below:

Blog: https://writingandbreathing.wordpress.com

Books: www.amazon.co.uk/-/e/B00RVO1BHO

Facebook: fb.me/margaretegrot.writer

Twitter: https://twitter.com/meegrot.

*

John Greatrex. John's poem about An Arundel Tomb featured in this anthology, was sent to Philip Larkin in 1983 to which he received a pleasant reply. Their correspondence, reported in The Coventry Observer, can be found by googling: 'Coventry Observer An Arundel Tomb'.

His poems have been aired professionally at Alan Ayckbourn's theatre in Scarborough, 'The Stephen Joseph Theatre In The Round'. He has also been awarded the Nottingham Poetry Prize – an annual competition organised by the Nottingham Poetry Society. He has also performed with the Lincolnshire Rock Gospel Group, Carillon, during their tour of the East Midlands.

John's verse play Joseph and His Amazing Crystal Palace, performed in schools and libraries in London and the East Midlands, tells the story of Coventry MP Joseph Paxton designer of Coventry's London Road Cemetery.

He is keen on performance poetry, inspired originally by the poets Alastair Aston, Patricia Doubell and Sydney Carter at The Crown and Greyhound Pub in Dulwich Village, South London.

More recently John was a headline poet at 'The First Thursday In The Month' Fire and Dust poetry open mic sessions which take place, like our Coventry Writers' Group, in The Big Comfy Bookshop, Far Gosford Street. When John isn't writing and performing poetry, his day job is on the checkouts at Sainsbury's.

*

Hilary Hopker works in communications for a large police force and is often inspired to write about crime and vulnerable people. She writes short stories, flash fiction, poetry and theatre reviews. She has won several writing prizes, been long and shortlisted in regional and national competitions and been published in national magazines and anthologies.

Hilary is also a watercolour painter and paints landscapes, both of Cornwall and Coventry. She has exhibited several times at University Hospital Coventry and Warwickshire and in the Coventry Open. She has painted the cover of this anthology, which is of Bayley Lane, a street near to the Cathedral in the city centre . To see more of her artwork check out @hopkerhilary on Instagram.

Margaret Mather was born and brought up in a small village on the west coast of Scotland. As a child, she had no great ambitions to be a writer but she loved to read. Heidi, Child of the Mountains, was her favourite story. It inspired a sense of adventure in her and at seventeen, with six pounds in her pocket, she left home to become an au pair in Norway.

On her return from Norway, Margaret moved to Coventry then to Nuneaton where she now lives. She first started writing many years ago as a hobby but never thought that anyone would want to read her work. After retiring from a long career as a business development manager in logistics, she found she had time on her hands and a head full of stories.

Margaret has had articles and stories printed in many magazines. From memory pieces published in *Scottish Memories* and *Yours Magazine* to articles printed in *Best of British*, *The People's Friend*, *Landscape* and many more.

A few years ago, she wrote and performed her own comedy sketch, mentored by comedian, Janice Connolly, at the Albany theatre in Coventry. She found it to be a frightening, yet enjoyable experience.

In addition to the articles and stories she writes, Margaret has now turned her hand to theatre reviewing and loves the adrenalin rush of a deadline. She has also written her first novel and is in the process of editing it.

Most of all, Margaret, takes pleasure from telling a good story and hopes her writing will go from strength to strength.

*

Nuzo Onoh is described as "The Queen of African Horror". Nuzo Onoh is a Nigerian-British writer of horror fiction from the African Continent. Her books have introduced African Horror to the international stage. Now recognised as the front-runner of African Horror, Nuzo has featured on numerous media platforms, spearheading this exciting horror subgenre.

She attended *Queen's School Enugu*, Nigeria, the Quaker's *The Mount School,* York, and *St Andrew's Tutorial College,* Cambridge, from where she obtained her A levels. Nuzo holds both a Law degree and a Masters degree in Writing from *The University of Warwick*. A keen musician, Nuzo plays both the piano and guitar, and holds an NVQ in Digital Music Production from *City College, Coventry*.

Nuzo is included in the book, *80 Black Women in Horror*, and her stories have also appeared in numerous anthologies. Her contest-winning story, *Guardians*, (Nosetouch Asterisk Anthology, Vol 2), is the first African Cosmic Horror story published. Her works also feature in academic studies, including the *"Routledge Handbook of African Literature"*. She has written several blogs for *Female First Magazine* and given talks and lectures on African Horror, including at *The Miskatonic Institute of Horror Studies in London*.

Website: www.nuzoonoh.com

Twitter: @Nuzoonoh

*

Mary Ogilvie. Since becoming a member of Coventry Writers' Group, Mary says she has learnt much about the craft of writing. Being with other like-minded people has been both helpful and inspiring. Poetry, short stories, articles, play writing and being a Grassroots reporter for the local newspaper have all come from her pen. Over the years she has had a variety of different items published in magazines and newspapers, and she says she continues to learn.

Ann Evans began writing as a hobby whilst bringing up three children and helping her husband with his car repair business. Once her stories and articles started being accepted for publication, there was no stopping her. She began writing books for children leading to publication by Scholastic Children's Books, Usborne Publishing and others. She now has around 40 books to her name in a wide variety of genres: children's books, YA, reluctant teen readers, romance and crime/thriller. She also writes for some lifestyle and hobby magazines.

She was a Feature Writer for the Coventry Telegraph for 13 years, having 'sneaked in the back door' when they advertised for local Grassroots reporters. She went on to become a staff Feature Writer. Since then, her children's book, *The Beast* has won the Coventry Inspiration Book Awards Raring2Read category 2013. *Keeper,* was runner-up in these awards in 2018 and *A Little Secret* won the Rapid Reads 2019 in these awards. It is currently short listed in the Doncaster Reading Rampage 2021.

Ann is a member of the Romantic Novelists' Association, the Crime Writers' Association, the National Association of Writers in Education, the Society of Women Writers & Journalists, and the Coventry Writers' Group.

Ann Evans website and social media links.

Website: www.annevansbooks.co.uk

Facebook: https://www.facebook.com/annevansbooks/

Twitter: https://twitter.com/annevansauthor

Linked in: https://www.linkedin.com/in/ann-evans-7211714a/

*

Owen Jennings was born in the city in 1950. He is best known for writing ' The Plays in a Bag'. Where he goes into local pubs, conscripts the customers as cast and acts out a scene of Coventry myth and history.

*

Paul Monks is a writer/artist/musician from Coventry. He works for a household name company in a hard-to-explain job. He once had a play performed in a field and has self-published a fantasy novel, The Darkening Wall. He mostly writes songs at present and has two albums available on all the usual platforms.

*

Gwydion Williams is a retired Computer Analyst. Written a lot, but nothing so far published. You can find his work and more details at https://gwydionmadawc.com/

*

The Coventry Writers' Group normally meets on the first Tuesday of each month, from 8pm-10pm at The Big Comfy Bookshop, Fargo Village, Coventry CV1 5EA

Find us on Facebook: https://www.facebook.com/groups/CoventryWritersGroup

Follow us on Twitter: https://twitter.com/Cov_Writers

Printed in Great Britain
by Amazon